PURR-FECTION

A CAT'S TALE

*I hope you enjoy your cruise
as much as I enjoyed mine*

SAMURAI'S STORY

BY
RODNEY HOYLE

Rodney Hoyle

11/1/07

CEDAR PUBLISHING LTD
7 BRADDONS CLIFFE
BRADDONS HILL RD EAST
TORQUAY
DEVON TQ1 1HR
01803 296733

Cover and Illustrations by Steven Sosna.

ISBN   1-902654-13-7

Published in 2005 by Cedar Publishing Ltd, United Kingdom.

Printed and bound in Great Britain by Halstan & Co Ltd, Amersham Bucks.

DEDICATIONS

Very sincere thanks to my wife Diane for her patience and advice during the writing of this book, and for introducing me to Sammy. Above all, thanks for the 30 wonderful years we have been married.

Sincere thanks also to David and Jacqueline Barber for their help in encouraging me to go into print with this my first book, for editing and advising me in all aspects of self-publication.

To Sammy and all of the other cats with whom we have shared love and affection. We have learnt to appreciate the individual character of each one. They have each brought something irreplaceable into our lives.

Map Of Sammy's Village

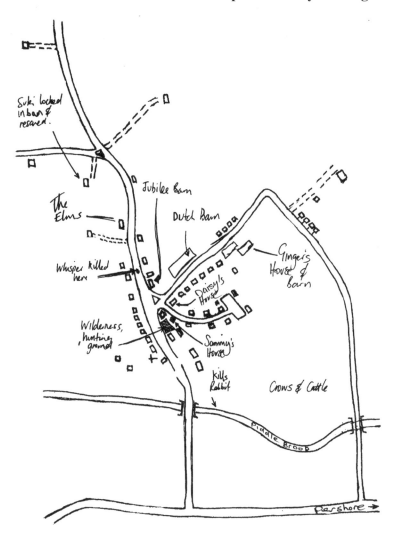

FORWARD

It is said that if you are lucky you have one really good dog in a lifetime. I count myself privileged that I had mine back in the 1960s, a black Labrador bitch called Jessica (Jessie) named after a film I had seen the night before I collected her.

At that time I was farming and Jessie accompanied me everywhere, becoming not only a companion but also the closest friend I could ever have wished for. I kept a twelve-bore shotgun permanently in the Land Rover and she was trained to the gun at an early age. She learnt to hunt in cover like a spaniel, point like a pointer, retrieve with the softest of mouths, swim like a fish and wait patiently at heel while driven birds fell all around her.

Many were the shoots I was invited to solely because of Jessie. Her soft mouth led to her losing a piece out of the end of her tongue after catching a rat in the farmyard and trying to carry it gently. She immediately learnt from this experience, and became an excellent rat catcher and killer. Her party trick was to find an egg hidden around the house and carry it back to me, depositing it unbroken into my hand. When Jessie died I vowed never to have another Labrador, knowing that she was irreplaceable.

During the 1970s, a short experience of owning an uncontrollable beagle put my wife off dogs forever. However, in 1985 she purchased a cat as a stress reliever for me. He had been born in May of that year to a half-Siamese father and a black farm cat mother. He grew up to be a Seal-point with a round head and solid body weighing around 5.5kilos (12lbs). I named him Samurai because I had just returned from a business trip to Japan. We were not to know it at the time but he grew to live up to the name, being a warrior right from the start and carrying his many battle scars with pride.

One of our neighbours, Dr Groom, was a very well-respected international cat judge who admired Samurai, once saying that he wished he had had the opportunity of breeding from him because he thought he could have been the beginning of a new breed of cat. Sadly, it was too late as he had already been neutered.

Samurai was our first cat, and he took to me immediately; he was a one-man cat, always jumping straight onto my lap when he came into the house. The greatest tribute to him is that he introduced us to cats. Since he arrived a further eight have at one time or another come into our household. Sadly, Sammy and three of the others have died. But we still have five living with us: Toby and Misty - Silver Tabby Persians, Pickwick and Dickens – Blue-point Birmans and Danny, a Seal-point Ragdoll.

This book was written five years after Samurai passed on. Memories of Sammy and Jessie are treasured; they are remembered as wonderful friends and great companions.

Rodney Hoyle
2005

CHAPTER ONE

THE FIRST SPRING OF MY LIFE

Dappled sunlight was filtering through the ventilation holes of the old tithe barn when I opened my eyes for the first time. There was a slight haze in the air as the flagstones warmed and the rising air lifted the accumulation of dust into the air.

The causes of the wonderful smells that I had known but which had been unseen for the past twelve days came into view. Bales of newly cut hay were stacked at the far end of the barn, giving off that wondrous aroma of early summer. A faint smell of diesel oil wafted from an old Ferguson tractor which stood in the middle. Two wooden barrels had been set down to one side, and from these came the mysterious smells of oak, port wine and apple cider. At our end of the barn were bales of last summer's straw. Our bed, an old white porcelain sink with the front mostly removed or broken away, stood on a few of them in the corner where it was warm and draught free.

It took me several minutes to take in my surroundings and then to notice that I had two brothers and a small sister. They were curled up together like an odd assortment of rags, sleeping between mother's front paws. One brother was mainly black like mother, with an odd white ear and white on both front paws, the other was tortoise shell, and my weakly sister was an indiscriminate brown with white patches. Mother was snoring in contentment and giving off a warm, milky smell that made me feel hungry. I crawled away from my siblings and trod gently against my mother's tummy to make the milk flow, then quickly attached my mouth to her teat and drank my fill.

In that first look at the world around me, I realised that I was the largest of our quartet of kittens and appeared to have an even, slightly golden covering of fur with darker patches on my feet and a darker tail. It must have been my contented purring that woke up the others, because there were a few quiet meows and they came crawling forward for their own milk. Mother gave a long yawn and told them to be careful not to scratch or bite her because it hurt. I crawled forward to show her my eyes were open. She licked my head gently and murmured, "I knew you were the strongest my little one. Listen well to my teachings and you will be all right." I purred with absolute pleasure and began to lick her front paw for the first time, before falling into a contented and satisfied sleep.

I awoke sometime later to the noise of the barn door being opened and saw an elderly lady with grey hair pulled back into a bun. She wore spectacles, a cotton apron over a summer dress and heavy brown shoes. Mother later told me this was Mrs Roberts who was very kind and brought her food every day. Mrs Roberts came over telling mother what a clever girl she was. Mother stretched in the leisurely way that only we cats know how to do, then leapt down onto the flagstone floor and began to ravenously consume the strange-smelling food that Mrs Roberts had emptied into a bowl from a tin she was holding. Mrs Roberts then lifted all four of us into a cardboard box and cleaned out the old sink, replacing the newspaper and straw. "There you are my darlings," she said as she lifted us up one by one and replaced us in our clean bed. She spent slightly longer looking at me, holding me up to the light and inspecting my mouth and eyes. "My, we are going to be a handsome boy aren't we," she murmured. Mother stopped eating for a moment and looked up at her as if to acknowledge that they both knew I was special, and then returned to lap up the milk from a saucer alongside her food bowl.

It was shortly after this that mother started teaching us how to wash our faces and ears, how to groom our coats and to tell us stories of the world outside the barn. Every so often, she would pick one of us up and take us to a damp spot in the other corner of the barn, trying to persuade of us to go to the toilet here, rather than soil our bedding. I could immediately see the sense in this and soon mastered the knack of holding on till she lifted me out. The others seemed to find the reason for this undignified exercise somewhat baffling, so I took it upon myself to cuff any individual that started to foul our nest. By now we were walking quite well, all that is, except our sister who was very weak and still crawled. She was obviously not strong enough to keep up with us boys. It was about this time that Mrs Roberts moved our porcelain home off the bales of straw to allow us to explore the floor and our surroundings. She also brought a tray full of some grey compound that mother said we were to use in future for our toilet. "House Training", she called it, but at that time it didn't mean anything to us.

About four weeks later we awoke one morning to hear mother crying, and soon realised that our little sister wasn't breathing any more. Mother explained that our little one had gone back to God and that we must all get on with our lives. Mrs Roberts came in later that morning and, full of "Ooh's" and "Aah's", took our sister away.

That night mother tried to explain death to us, and warned us of the many perils in the big world that could end our own lives. The next day Mrs Roberts brought some special food for my brothers and I; it tasted of fish and was mashed up into tiny pieces so we could eat it. "Come on little ones," she said, "special kitten food to make you grow big and strong." I was first to the bowl and sniffed the strange mixture, then put out my tongue for a little taste. Not bad was my first reaction, so I nibbled a bit more then let my brothers in for their turn. By now we were all happy to use the dirt tray, which Mrs Roberts cleaned out every day, and although she still changed the bedding daily it was now free from our little mistakes! So she replaced the newspaper and straw with a piece of warm blanket.

Mother warned us not to go out of the barn because of the dangers outside; she did however let us roam further and further away from our bed each day, although I know she kept an eye on us to ensure we didn't get into difficulty. By now we were playing games, chasing each other around our porcelain home and learning to grab hold of one another and roll and roll round and round amidst squeals of delight and frustration.

Mother started to show us other wonders in our small world. First it was a beetle that had come in after a rain shower. It had a wonderful dark blackish-purple shell. Mother showed us how to stalk it, then she batted it with her paw and it went rolling away. What fun! We all joined in and tossed it around the floor until it scuttled under a bale of hay. That night she showed us how to catch moths. Leaping and twisting, she literally took them out of the air. We were not big enough to do this as yet, but we were learning very quickly from our mother.

By the fifth week Mrs Roberts had brought some small balls into the barn. They had rattles inside, and we loved chasing them around the flagstone floor. It was during one of these playtimes, when mother was in our home with one eye upon us, that what to us was a huge strange cat crawled through a gap under the door of our barn. He was the most terrifying and yet beautiful creature any of us had ever seen. Taller, longer and slimmer than mother, his muscles rippled under his warm caramel-cream coloured coat. His ears, face, tail and paws were dark brown. In his mouth he carried a small furry creature with a long tail which mother later told me was a mouse. He stalked proudly across the barn towards mother, while we stopped our playing and watched in terror. She rose to her feet and walked slowly towards him. When they were a few paces apart he dropped the mouse and sidled slowly backwards away from it, allowing her to pick it up, turn her back and start crunching the bones of the tiny creature. The stranger stood quietly waiting and then moved forwards and nuzzled her ear. I heard her purr and realised that they were old friends. They talked quietly together for what seemed an age before mother called us forward, and introduced us to our father.

I soon became aware that this handsome creature must be very fond of our mother, and that the mouse had been a reward for looking after his children. On closer inspection, I saw several scars on his ears and face, and asked him where they had come from. He gave me a friendly cuff on the head with his paw which sent me sprawling and said, "You will find out for yourself how I got them. You'll have your own battle scars soon enough!" We thought he had come to live with us and skipped around him, only half listening to the words of advice he was trying to give us. Eventually he nuzzled up to mother again and walked towards the door. Suddenly he stopped and called to me. I ran to him immediately while my brothers stood watching. "You're going to be a fine strong young fellow," he said. "Remember me and your mother when they take you away. We won't forget you either. Be Top Cat my son. I know you have it in you. Learn to be the best hunter in the area. You can be, it just takes time, stealth and practice." With that he leant down, licked the top of my head, turned and in a moment was gone.

That was to be the one and only time I met my father, and in later years I came to know it was from him that I inherited my striking markings, blue eyes and my strength. But it was from my mother that I got my beautiful round head and more compact physique.

A few days later mother took us out of the barn to look at the outside world for the first time. It was so bright after the shadowy light in the barn. There were birds and butterflies, even a blue dragonfly by a small fishpond, all too fast for us kittens. There was the lovely thatched cottage where Mrs Roberts lived, with the smell of warm bread drifting through the window. We crept through the long grass in the field alongside the cottage, pretending that we were stalking mice. The sun shone down and warmed my coat, and I realised that I had an almost perfect camouflage, my caramel-cream coat, broken up by the dark of my ears, paws and tail, blended perfectly with the dried summer grass. In fact, I was so busy admiring myself that I nearly got left behind. Realising I was alone, I hurried after the others and caught them up just as they turned back along a path to the barn; we crept inside, crawled into our bed and soon fell into a contented sleep.

The next few weeks passed quickly. We fell into a pattern of sleeping, playing, eating, exploring and always listening and learning. I suppose that I was about eight weeks old when Mrs

Roberts came into the barn with two people; one was a smart lady wafting perfume and the other a grey-haired man who smelt of pipe tobacco. They picked each of us up in turn, and I heard the man say he liked my big paws and thought that I would be ideal. They turned and left the barn, and I was left wondering what it was all about. Mother softly called me over and said my time was nearly up. I didn't know what she meant until she explained that it had happened before when someone had come and taken one of her kittens away, but I was not to be afraid, and I was to remember my father's words.

Over the following weeks, we were weaned onto the tinned kitten food provided by the kindly Mrs Roberts and grew bigger and stronger each day. Mother spent more and more time away from the barn hunting on her own. Her coat took on a beautiful sheen and, with her round head and green eyes, she was the most beautiful black cat you could ever wish to see.

Four weeks after their first visit the couple returned, this time carrying a cardboard box. Mrs Roberts picked me up and, without a word to mother, handed me to the man. For the first time in my life I felt the comfort of the caress of a human being. He stroked me gently and kept talking to me before handing me to his partner who, I later learnt, was his wife. She cuddled me, and for a moment I felt quite safe. Then, without warning, I was bundled into the cardboard box and, screaming for my mother, carried out of the barn and placed into a car. I continued to scream and scratch to get out, but couldn't hear a sound from mother or my brothers. I heard the man agree a price of five pounds and then he and his wife climbed into the car.

I cannot describe the fear I felt, suddenly torn away from my family and the familiar environment that I had come to know so well, thrust into a dark box and driven away surrounded by strange smells.

It didn't take long before the car stopped and I was lifted out and carried into a strange building. I didn't know it then, but this was to be home for the rest of my life.

The man carefully lifted me out of the cardboard box, held me gently in his arms, stroked my head and started talking to me. "Calm down little man, this is your new home and we are your new Dad and Mum. You are going to be called Samurai, and that's a proud name for a proud cat," he chuckled. Later on I heard them talking to friends and discovered that the samurai were members of an ancient Japanese warrior class.

Having stroked and talked to me for a few minutes, he handed me to the lady. She sat on a kitchen chair and tried to calm me down. I remember her grip loosening slightly and, seizing my chance, I leapt to freedom. I landed on the run and found myself on a shiny tiled kitchen floor which was difficult to grip with my paws. I scampered through an open door into a utility room with various cupboards and machines, headed towards a corner and spotted a very small gap where the bases of two cupboards met. I heard them running after me and, as they came through the door, I squeezed myself through the tiny space into a dark recess. The floor of the cupboard was above me and the platform supporting it ran round all the sides. The only way in or out was through the tiny hole which I had entered. Their voices came drifting to me, calling "Come on

Samurai." "Come on Sammy." I cowered in the darkness and heard the man go away. Then he returned, bringing with him the smell of my food. He was trying to tempt me out, but I was far too scared to move. They next tried going away and ignoring me in the hope that curiosity would bring me out. But unknown to them, tiredness and fear got the better of me and I curled myself up into a ball and soon fell into an uneasy sleep.

I woke to the most awful noise. The man was starting to dismantle the front of my refuge with the help of a hammer, a screwdriver and a lot of very bad language. Realising that I had only moments before I was caught, I made a quick exit through the gap and ran back into the kitchen pursued by a very angry, red-faced man! This time I saw a space beside the cooker, dived into it and crawled into a rather smelly and cobwebby area behind it. I heard them discussing what to do next. They finally decided to reassemble the base of the unit in the utility room and fill the gap into my first hiding place. Sometime later they moved the cooker forward, retrieved me from my second hiding place and took me into a large comfortable lounge, where there was a lovely wicker basket with the blanket from my first home tucked neatly into the bottom. I was placed into this basket and immediately became aware of the comforting smell of my mother and brothers. You may think that this would have upset me, but I found it very reassuring and, after all my excitement, once again curled myself into a ball and fell asleep.

I awoke later to the reassuring smell of the blanket mixed with the faint aroma of cooking from the kitchen. I lay there quietly, realising that the plan I had formulated over the past weeks had failed. Knowing that I was to be taken away from my family in the barn, I had decided that the minute I arrived at my intended new home I would instigate immediate maximum disruption aimed at forcing them to take me back to my home in the tithe barn.

Well I had tried and failed in that. Should I now put into action part two by ignoring the litter tray I had seen in the utility room, and instead commence using carpets and corners as my toilet?

This went very much against my nature and, looking around at the comfortable surroundings and contemplating the couple that I might have to adopt, I began to realise that there might be many advantages over the life I had had in the barn. So I decided it might be best to endure a couple more days of accli-matisation before resorting to this more drastic action.

With this in mind I stood up, stretched and wandered out to the tray to perform my duties in regular fashion. Then I drank a little water from a bowl on the floor and nibbled at some kitten food left in a saucer, before setting out to explore my new accommodation.

On closer inspection, the kitchen was large and airy with big windows, a quarry tile floor, cupboards and drawers in a warm wood finish, a breakfast bar and an eating area with four chairs, against which I rubbed my neck to leave my scent and mark my territory. I ambled from there into a small study where there was a red sofa, an armchair and a large black box with a sort of window in it, which I later came to know as a television. This room had a beige carpet and led into a large hall with a staircase leading to a higher level, and wood-block flooring with a big rug in the middle. To the left was a dining room with a large table, six chairs, and wall cabinets displaying ornaments, glassware and photographs. The carpet was similar to the one in the study.

I wandered back into the lounge, where my basket was still on the floor. This room was very large and carpeted in a similar fashion to the other two rooms. There was a large window at the front and a big French window at the other end through which I could see a pretty garden. At one side was a fireplace containing a large log-burning stove with a copper canopy, and not far from it another of those black boxes with a screen. There were two armchairs in a beige colour and a matching four-seater sofa. I scent-marked all of these, and was now happy that my territory was established. The chairs looked very comfortable and, since I preferred to be higher off the floor, I climbed into the nearest one. It was a bit too high for me to jump straight into, but with one leap and the help of my claws I clambered up, made myself comfortable on its warm, soft upholstery, and snuggled up against a cushion. It appeared that my adopted parents had gone out for a short while, so once more I settled down for a snooze.

I woke up to the sound of children's voices: "Mummy isn't he lovely? Can I pick him up? How old is he?" The questions tumbled out of the lips of a little girl of about eight years old. With her was a shy little boy, wide-eyed in amazement. I soon learnt that they were Carolyn and Christopher, and that their mum and dad were called Rod and Diane. The little girl picked me up and cuddled me whilst the boy approached carefully and began to stroke my head. Things were beginning to take a turn for the better. It began to look as though I had exchanged life in the tithe barn with my mother and two brothers for a new family of my own, four people that I could adopt and adapt to my own ways.

After a few minutes, Carolyn handed me to her brother and went upstairs to her bedroom. Christopher sat down on the chair where I had been sleeping and snuggled up to me holding me rather tight, until Diane took me away from him and sent him upstairs to change his clothes. A little later Rod returned from work, asked where I was and came into the lounge. He picked me up from the chair where I was sitting, sat down, put me onto his knee and started stroking my head and back. I purred, and he smiled and said what a happy kitten I must be, that I had been bought as a stress-reliever and that it was my job to soothe his nerves.

A little later he lit his pipe and relaxed into the chair, still gently stroking me. I think it was at this moment that it dawned on me this was going to be the one person in the family I would really own, and I should make every effort to make him love me. Moving my head slightly, I nuzzled into his hand asking for more affection, and he responded with more strokes just as I wanted. Now I knew we had already established a special bond because I, too, was beginning to feel affection for this man.

Sometime later Diane called the family into the kitchen for their supper, and I followed to watch what was going on before wandering into the utility room to satisfy my own hunger pangs. A little later, after the clatter of dishes being washed up,

Rod came and picked me up, and we returned to the chair in the lounge. He re-lit his pipe, picked up something from the table beside him, pushed a button on it, and suddenly sounds and pictures appeared on the screen of the box in the corner of the room. I stayed where I was for a few minutes then began to get a slightly trapped and uneasy feeling, so I jumped down and wandered across to the basket which they had placed beside one of the chairs, settled down on the blanket and fell asleep.

I don't remember much more about that first evening other than that the children picked me up and cuddled me before going to bed. A few hours later I was taken into the utility room where the basket was placed on the floor, fresh water and kitten food provided, the light was turned off and the door closed, and I was left to spend the first night of my life sleeping on my own. I must confess that I did cry for a while but eventually I fell into an exhausted sleep; it had been a busy day.

During the following days life fell into a pattern. Rod would leave home at about 8:15 for work, and Diane looked after the children who were enjoying the summer holidays. Rod returned from work about six in the evening and always greeted the family before looking for me, picking me up and going into the lounge to smoke his pipe, watch the news on television and gently stroke my head. As the days turned into weeks, memories of the barn faded into the distance and I settled into this very happy routine with my adopted family.

I was by now growing at a swift rate. It wasn't long before I was able to climb the staircase and both explore and scent-mark the new territory upstairs. There was not much of interest up there. The only time I curled up and fell asleep on one of the comfy beds I was unceremoniously picked up by Diane and dumped out on the landing, so I realised that she disapproved of my being in the bedrooms.

It was after about three weeks of this routine around the house that on a sunny Saturday I was allowed into the garden for the first time. Rod picked me up and carried me outside, placed me gently on the grass and told me not to wander off. The children were playing on a swing and slide, and Diane and Rod had placed garden chairs on the lawn. Once I had taken in the various strange odours around me, instinct told me to extend my territory. I wandered over to a large tree and rubbed my neck up against it leaving my first marker behind. I moved on to the post of a pergola and repeated the performance, then to a flowerpot and a small greenhouse. Within ten minutes I had marked this area as my own, firstly to advise other animals that there was a newcomer around and secondly to guide me home if I should get lost. Rod had placed my basket out on the lawn so, exhausted by my morning activities, I was happy to curl up in it and, warmed by the mid-summer sun, fell sound asleep.

It was now just after the middle of August. I calculate that I had been born in the middle of May so I was about sixteen weeks old. I awoke one morning to find lots of excitement in the house; Diane came into the utility room, picked me up and tied a big red ribbon round my neck. She then carried me upstairs into the bedroom and handed me to Rod saying, "Happy Birthday!" He laughed and said that he didn't think the ribbon suited me, but that I was the best present he had ever received. He then removed the ribbon and pulled me closer for a cuddle.

It rained most of that day and we stayed indoors. The children spent some time rolling balls to me and trailing pieces of cotton for me to chase. Rod had lots of cards and a few other presents then they all sat down for a special supper in the evening while I lay snugly in my basket. By now all thoughts of wishing to return to the tithe barn had disappeared.

It was a few days later when, to my horror, Rod picked me up and placed me back into the cardboard box in which they had first collected me. I was sure that I had done something wrong and that I was being taken back to Mrs Roberts, but by now this was the last thing I wanted. He placed the box inside his car and we drove off. It wasn't long before we stopped, and the box was carried into a place that smelt of strange animals. I could hear a cat crying, and loud snuffling noises came from something much bigger. A few minutes later I was moved into another room, the box was opened by Rod and I saw a strange man in a white coat. He picked me up, examined my coat and stomach, looked into my ears and mouth and declared that I was a good healthy kitten. He said I appeared to be an unusual long-haired oriental, and that I should be given an injection for feline enteritis, rhinotracheitis and calcivirus. Then he produced an instrument which he filled with fluid from a bottle and, lifting the skin of my neck, stuck something into me which stung slightly. "There we are," he said, handing Rod a small packet. "Give him this pill and it will soon see to any worms. If you're going to have him neutered, I suggest at about six months old. You can book it with the receptionist on the way out if you want." Little did I know what was store for me a few weeks hence! With that I was placed back into the box, and taken home.

That evening Rod prepared a bit of cheese for me, rolling it into a ball and trying to conceal the worm pill in the middle. He placed it on the floor and, to aggravate him for the indignity I had suffered from the man in the white coat, I picked the cheese up in my mouth, worked the pill out of the middle, spat it out and swallowed the cheese. He tried again with a larger piece of cheese, and I repeated the process. By now the pill was wet and slimy. When he retrieved it from the floor, he called Diane and asked her to hold me while he popped the pill into my mouth. While Diane gripped me tightly and held my front paws together so that I couldn't scratch her, Rod squeezed my cheeks till my mouth opened and popped the pill onto the back of my tongue. He then held my mouth shut with one hand and stroked my throat with the other; I manoeuvred the pill into my cheek so that when he released me I could spit it out once again.

At that point he gave up and went to smoke his pipe to calm down. I never did see that pill again, but I suspect that it got mixed in with my kitten food, because the following day I had an awful tummy ache. So maybe if I did have worms they had been eliminated.

By now we were in late August. The weather was overcast with sunny intervals, but warm and dry. They started to let me out in the garden for short periods on my own, and this gave me the opportunity of exploring a little further afield each time, marking my way accordingly. I discovered that on one side our garden was separated from the next by a tall, panelled fence. Sometimes I heard noises from a large animal, and even a loud growl when I tried to attract its attention. This must be one of those dogs that mother had warned me about, so I omitted that area from my territory. At the end of the house was a long lawned garden, on one side of which was a beech hedge bordering the drive leading to the house. There was a short hedge on the other side of the lawn beyond which was a wilderness of long grass, nettles, brambles and tumbledown buildings.

This was a most promising area to explore, and I soon plucked up the courage to venture into the dense undergrowth. As I slowly crept forward, pushing the long grass and weeds aside, I picked up the smell of mice, and all around I could hear small birds singing. Above me, swallows swooped in the sky, plucking small insects from the air. Away to one side a frog croaked, so I moved in that direction first and came to a small overgrown pond. I lapped at the water but it had a peculiar taste and the water in my own bowl was far superior.

The frog was sitting on a stone at the far side watching me, but as soon as I made to move in his direction he dived into the pond. I suppose that I must have been standing quite still because, just as I was about to leave, a small bird landed a few feet in front of me and began to dip its head up and down into the water. I slowly lowered my belly onto the ground, gathered my rear legs forward, tensed my muscles, wriggled my bottom and, swishing my tail in excitement, prepared to spring. The bird must have sensed danger, because it stopped drinking and raised its head, then stood still, listening. Fearing that it was about to fly away, I sprang. My sharp claws met only fresh air as, with an angry chirp, the bird flew into the distance, leaving a tail feather drifting in the breeze.

Disheartened, I made my way back through the undergrowth to my own home, and lay on the terrace in the sunshine to ponder what I had done wrong. I soon came to the conclusion that there were some positive aspects to my first hunting expedition. Firstly, I had found a spot where birds came to drink; secondly, I had learnt to be more careful and not to frighten my prey. And lastly I had discovered that I must not let my excitement make me move too soon. I remembered my father's words and that I must not get disheartened. I must be patient, learn stealth and practise if I was to be the best hunter around.

The next day I retraced my steps to the pond, where I could hear the frog croaking again. I felt that it was time to put my thoughts into action and see how close I could get to Mr Frog without him knowing I was there. With this in mind, and remembering that his stone was on the far side of the pond, I circled round to the right of the water in order to approach him from behind, keeping low to the ground and moving very slowly through the long grass and nettles. The sound of his croaking was very near but I still could not see him. After another few feet, the undergrowth began to thin out and suddenly there he was, about four feet in front of me and completely unaware of my presence. I moved clear of the last of the long grass into a clearing just behind him. Slithering inch-by-inch, careful to keep my tail flat, my bottom still and my breathing quiet, I moved to within my own length of him and stopped. Gathering my hind legs under me for power, I paused for a second and sprang; I swear he didn't know what hit him! My judgement and timing were superb, claws and teeth bit into him simultaneously, and he was dead in an instant. Unfortunately, I had not taken into account the power of my spring and the resulting momentum for, with front claws and mouth firmly around the frog, I cleared the stone and went head first into the green, smelly water.

I seemed to stay under forever, but then with a few strong kicks from my back legs, I surfaced, spluttering and struggling to hold the frog in my mouth. It was with considerable effort that I floundered back to the bank, satisfied that I had at least made my first kill. I put the frog down and examined him more closely. He was ugly and slimy but I thought he would taste all right. How wrong I was. Uugh, he tasted bitter and horrible! And I thought that perhaps I would leave frog off the menu in future.

I heard Rod calling my name and retraced my steps into our garden. He was standing on the terrace and when he saw the bedraggled state I was in he became most concerned. He took me indoors complaining about the smell, put some soap and water into a bowl, and subjected me to the indignity of a bath, later drying me on a nice warm towel. I felt this was a poor reception for a famous hunter!

CHAPTER TWO

AUTUMN

By now it was early September, the days were gradually getting shorter and the weather was a little cooler. I was now about eighteen weeks old, but I'm very sure that I was large for my age. I had the most beautiful Seal-point markings to my ears, paws and tail, a round face, which was almost black, and deep blue eyes. The rest of my coat was still a caramel-cream colour, with medium length hair that shone like silk. I was growing bigger, stronger and braver with each day that passed, and I was gradually extending the range of my daily explorations.

It was about then that Rod came home one weekend with a package and told me he had bought me a present. He spent most of the morning on his hands and knees by the back door with various tools that I had not seen before. First he cut a hole at the bottom of the door and then, with much cursing and swearing, he finally managed to attach a device to the opening and proudly announced: "There you are Sammy, your own cat flap. All you've got to do now is learn how to use it!"

Then he picked me up and, despite my struggling, pushed me through the hole and onto the terrace outside. He then came outside to join me. Diane stayed inside, closed the door and, holding a bowl of food on the other side where I could see and smell it through the clear flap, raised the flap inwards with her hand. Rod put my front paws onto the ledge at the bottom of the flap and pushed me inside. They praised me and said that I could have my dinner when I could do it on my own. Rod then went out and closed the door. Through the clear plastic flap, I could see him place my bowl of food on the floor. I tried to move the flap with my paw but it seemed to be stuck so, pushing with the top of my head, I felt it swing away and I scrambled through. They repeated the process several times, and when they were satisfied that I had mastered the device, left me to eat the food and kept telling me that I was a very clever boy.

It didn't take me long to realise that I now had my own private way in and out of the utility room, and that during the day I was now allowed to come and go as I pleased. For the next couple of months they did something that stopped it working at night and kept me in the utility room.

During the next week it became clear why the cat flap had been fitted. On the following Monday morning Diane dressed early and set off just after Rod to take Carolyn to school and Christopher to a childminder. Then she went to work leaving me at home on my own. It seemed to me as though Diane had not worked during the two and a half years since Chris had been born. Now that he was old enough to be looked after by a childminder, she was able to go back to work. On Mondays and Thursdays she worked six hours a day. I was to spend these two days each week on my own, and this gave me plenty of time to continue my explorations and to perfect my hunting technique. On these days, she came home in the late afternoon after collecting the children. On the other three days of the week she took Carolyn to school while Chris stayed with her as she did the housework, cooking and shopping.

The following week I covered all of the ground and buildings on the side of the garden containing Frog's Pond. There were various tumbledown sheds of brick, wood and corrugated iron, and these had plenty of signs of small animals either living in them or passing through. I once saw a small mouse but it was too quick for me. There was some evidence of another cat marking territory and this made me wary so I over-marked with my own scent, and hoped that I would not meet formidable opposition too soon.

I moved on up the garden towards a black and white house with a dilapidated bothy and the ruins of a couple of pigsties which quite obviously had not been used for many years. It was full of cobwebs, and birds were nesting under the tiled roof. I continued by the left-hand side of the house and, passing the other end of my garden, I could now see through a chain-link fence into the garden that was concealed from mine by the fence panels. Lying on a lawn was a very large brown and black dog with a thick muzzle and short, stubby tail. I crouched low so as not to be seen and studied him for a few moments. I later learnt that this was Marcus, a Rottweiler who surprisingly enough was never a problem to me or anyone I knew. The man he owned, Dr Groom, took him for a walk twice a day, keeping him on a lead, so that he never got into trouble. I kept going in the same direction and passed the bottom of another garden. Here Sheba, a Golden Labrador, saw me and charged up to the fence barking. I ignored her and went on my way, passing by the deserted garden of a final house and up to a metal gate. I crawled under this gate, went up a short path and found myself at the end of a road which served the four houses on our side. Opposite were three bungalows, then a lawn with some low net fencing, alongside which was part of the garden of a house almost opposite my own. It was here that I saw a grey tabby cat not much bigger than myself. She saw me at the same time and, with fur and hackles raised, came slowly towards me.

I stopped on the path beside the road and waited as she came closer. I heard her growl and, rather than upset her, I rolled onto my back in submission. She approached me very slowly through a gap under the fence, and I whispered, "Hello, who are you?" She told me that her name was Daisy and that I was to stay off her patch. Then she came over, sniffed my coat and asked where I had come from. I said that I was from the other side of the beech hedge just over the road. "Well, then we are neighbours," said Daisy. "It might be best if we keep out of each other's gardens till we get to know each other better." I agreed to this proposal and slowly turned onto my front. She really was quite pretty with dark and light grey markings and twinkling green eyes. She asked me my name and how long I had been around. I in turn found out that she was six months older than me, and that she had a companion whom I should avoid at all costs. He was a liver and white cocker spaniel called Higgins, and Daisy had a very low opinion of him. "Have you tried hunting in the Dutch barn at Poplars Farm?" she enquired. I replied that I didn't know where that was. "Oh, come on Sammy, I'll show you now. Follow me, but be careful."

She turned and walked off down the path, over a narrow lane and a ditch, through a thin hedge that brought us out on the edge of a farmyard, and alongside an open-sided barn, stacked high with bales of straw and hay. Daisy crept quietly into the barn, scrambled up onto some of the higher bales and indicated for me to follow. I climbed up and settled down beside her to wait. She asked me to keep absolutely silent and wait to see what happened.

After a few minutes there was a rustling noise a few bales below us, and a small grey mouse crept out looking for little bits of grain trapped in the straw. I watched in fascination as he nibbled away at the twine on the bale until it parted with a snap and the bale sprang open, allowing the mouse to scramble inside. Daisy suggested that I demonstrate my hunting skills to her, saying that she would get him if I missed.

Determined to impress this young lady, I slid silently towards the open bale and saw the tail end of the mouse so intent on filling himself with the newly exposed grain that he had thrown caution to the wind. I closed in and sprang with fine judgement, trapping him under my paw and transferring him swiftly to my mouth. I looked at Daisy who had moved silently behind me and saw her smiling in admiration at my skill. "Come on, let's have a game with him. Bring him down," she instructed, leaping down to the farmyard below. "Bring him over here," she said, and I did as I was told, moving into a space where the grass had been flattened by tractor tyres. "Let him go, then catch him again," she said. Again I obeyed, placing the mouse gently on the floor and opening my mouth. With a squeak he dashed away and I caught him with my left foot and tossed him into the air. He landed by Daisy who batted him back to me. There was some blood on his shoulder where my claws had caught him. Undeterred I pounced on him again, held him between my paws until he recovered a little, then let him go again. His second run for freedom was a little slower than the first, and there was no need to throw him this time. I just chased after him and knocked him over before he got too far, then turned around and repeated the process. This continued for several minutes until he was too exhausted to run and the fun went out of the game. I once again picked him up in my mouth and carried him to Daisy as a present, in the same way my father had done for mother. "No Sammy," she smiled. "This one is not for me. Take it to the people you own, and let them know what a good hunter you are."

So telling her I would see her soon, I retraced my steps to where I had met her, crossed over the road and crawled through the beech hedge back into my own garden. The mouse had by now expired, so I crawled through the cat flap with him in my mouth and left him on the utility room floor. I felt hot, tired and dusty so, after a quick drink to clean the mouse taste out of my mouth, I climbed into my basket, washed myself from tail to nose and fell into a satisfied sleep.

I was woken by Chris shouting: "Mummy, Mummy, Sammy's got a nanimul!" I sat up, proudly awaiting my praise. Diane rushed out and shrieked, pushed Chris away from it and, grabbing a piece of tissue from her pocket, picked my trophy off the floor by the tail and carried it outside. She came back telling me that I was naughty and not to bring things home. Then off she went followed by Carolyn and Chris to bury my present in the garden, too deep for me to dig up and eat. What a waste!

The next morning after breakfast, I set out through the beech hedge to try to find Daisy. But there was no sign of her so I continued on my way to the barn where yesterday's fun had been so good. I climbed up to our previous lookout and looked down to see if there was any sign of further activity around the broken bale, but all was quiet at present. I lay down and waited patiently. Sparrows were flitting in and out of the open-sided barn, and several doves sat cooing on the roof of a large brick-built barn at the side of the farmyard. In the distance, rooks called to each other in their strange language. I think their young were about to leave the nest for the first time, because there seemed to be great excitement. I was almost asleep when a movement right at the bottom of the straw bales caught my attention. I perked up and saw a large grey animal with a very long tail which hung down to the ground behind him. He had a large pointed face with long whiskers, and looked wicked. This was no mouse! I was seeing a rat for the first time. To me he looked huge and menacing, and I was quite frightened. There was no way I was going to pick a fight with Mister Rat. Little did I know that I was looking at a formidable adversary, many of whose kind I was to kill in the years to come. This time discretion was the better part of valour, so I watched him slink into the big brick barn and disappear.

Shortly after this, Daisy came sauntering around the corner. I meowed quietly to attract her attention, and she leapt up beside me, gave me a quick sniff and lay down. A few minutes later, a large ginger cat appeared from behind the farmhouse. Daisy urged me to be silent and to keep as still and as low as possible. We watched him cross the farmyard towards the brick barn. As he reached the point where the rat had been, his nose went down. He turned and followed its scent, disappearing into the barn a few moments later.

Daisy advised that we stay where we were and await developments. These didn't take long. Within a few minutes, we heard a scuffle from the barn, a loud squeal, and then silence. Ginger reappeared about five minutes later, holding the now dead rat in his mouth by the scruff of its neck and dragging it along with him. At that moment an elderly lady came out of the door of the farmhouse with a broom in her hand. She spotted Ginger and his kill and shouted into the house for help. A short, stout elderly man wearing a cap and smoking a pipe joined her. He walked down the steps from the house and called to the ginger cat, who promptly dropped the rat and sprinted off round the back of the house. The man laughed then went into a shed, returning a few moments later with a spade and a paper sack. He scooped the rat up with the spade, popped it into the sack and deposited it into a dustbin at the top of the steps. Then he stopped to light his pipe, turned to survey the yard, opened the door and went inside.

The whole incident had only taken about ten minutes, and Daisy later explained that Ginger was the most feared bully in the village and best avoided at all times. She said that he lived at a farm further up the lane, but he considered anywhere to be his territory. She told me to keep well clear of him until I was old enough to look after myself. She also told me that the elderly couple were a farmer and his wife who owned some of the adjacent fields, keeping mostly sheep and lambs. The big barn was called The Jubilee Barn. The farmer used it for lambing in the spring and local residents sometimes used it for barn dances. I hoped that he got Ginger to clear the rats out before they did that!

Since the coast was now clear, we wandered back towards our respective homes. Diane was on the path outside the house where Daisy lived, talking to the lady that Daisy owned. Chris was in the garden playing with Higgins the liver and white springer spaniel, throwing a ball for him and shouting out "Fetch, Piggings!" as he couldn't pronounce the dog's name correctly.

Higgins dashed across the lawn, retrieved the ball and bounded back to Chris who was jumping up and down with excitement, collided with him and sent the little boy flying. Chris picked himself up and ran to Diane complaining that Piggings was a naughty boy. She picked Chris up, said her goodbyes, and we all returned home.

September days flew by, and the weather turned colder and more overcast. I stayed in the house on the frequent rainy days, but I made the most of my hunting skills on the better ones. Daisy and I continued to meet and catch our fair share of mice. She showed me how to hunt voles in the hedgerows, and we both managed to keep clear of rats and Ginger the bully.

I had by now established a good rapport with Rod, and spent most evenings curled up on his lap while he smoked his pipe and watched television. They changed my diet from kitten to cat food, which I much preferred, and every evening before I went to bed they gave me a handful of something called Munchies, which really were tasty. Now that the nights were cooler they brought my basket into the kitchen, and Rod fitted another cat flap to the kitchen door so that I could go out to the litter tray in the utility room. I didn't need to use the tray on the days I spent outside, only when the weather kept me indoors. I began to appreciate that I was a very lucky young cat: I had a warm and comfortable home, plenty of space outside in which to hunt, a very good friend in Daisy and I owned a kind and loving family. Thoughts of my mother and brothers faded into a distant memory.

One night towards the end of September, Rod forgot to lock the outer cat flap. The night became quite windy and I woke to hear the noise of the flap blowing in the wind, I decided to investigate. Seeing the flap open, I pushed my way through it and, for the first time, I was out on my own at night. I stood still for a while just taking in the different sounds. There were no birds singing. In the distance, I could hear traffic on the roads, and the hoot of an owl. Something similar to a dog barked and small animals moved in the wilderness behind our garden. Overhead, bats flew and caught small insects. Something larger was moving in the hedge just over the back lawn and I went to investigate. Moving silently and crouching low, I approached and heard a snuffling noise. I peered into the bottom of the hedge where there was a layer of dead leaves, and I saw the most extraordinary animal. It was slightly smaller than me, a darkish-brown colour with a long snout, small piggy eyes and very short legs. But instead of a silky feline coat, it had long spikes lying flat all over its body.

It looked fairly harmless so I decided to attack, and without further ado I leapt at it. It responded by folding its head underneath itself and elevating the spines, which I quickly discovered had very sharp spikes on the end. Some of these buried themselves in the soft pads of my front paws, causing excruciating pain. I whimpered, and moved a short distance away to lick my wounds before returning to try another tactic. Since the animal had hidden its head underneath its body, I decided to try and turn it over. Approaching it again I could still hear a snuffling noise coming from beneath, so I carefully put my paw under it, avoiding the spines, and flicked it onto its back. Imagine my surprise when the whole thing turned into a spiky ball! There was no way of attacking this, so I gave it up as a bad job and thought that I would just put it down to experience. Thinking that this was the end of the matter, I spent the next couple of hours hunting voles in the wilderness area with great success. I'm not sure, but believe my score was five killed and two frightened nearly to death. Later on I returned to my bed well contented.

It was not until several days later that the itching started. It felt as though I had things running about in my coat, and not only did they make me itch but they also bit me occasionally. Every time I felt them I stopped, scratched and inspected my coat carefully. Eventually I spotted one, a small reddish-brown insect that scuttled away. Day after day I tried to catch them without success, and I became more and more uncomfortable.

A few days later Rod felt one bite him and the culprits were finally identified: fleas! The next day Diane came home with something she had purchased from the vet. She held me while Rod sprayed me with a foul-smelling substance and then combed it into my coat. Then they sprayed my bedding, the carpets and the chairs where I slept. They sprayed me once a week for the next month until I was finally free of the legacy of the hedgehog. Another lesson learnt and another creature to avoid.

Once or twice on my travels, I saw long-tailed grey squirrels darting up the walnut trees. They were too big and quick for me to catch, but I was sure they would still be there when I got bigger.

During that first year I found it difficult to understand the changing seasons. As I explained, I had been born in May, so had the long balmy days of summer in which to develop both my body and mind. I had noticed the shortening of the days and changes of weather during September, but now that October was here, dramatic things were happening. The days were noticeably shorter, with the mornings often damp and misty. The beech hedge was changing from green to golden brown; the pear trees in the garden had lost the last of their pears on one windy night, and were now shedding their leaves. Summer flowers had faded, and the garden furniture and barbecue had been packed away. In October, I saw my first frost on the lawn, and it felt cold through my tender pads. There were blackberries on the hedge in the lane, and the mice in the barn seemed more eager than ever to fatten themselves up before winter set in - which meant the sport was better than ever. I was now twenty-two weeks old, and a fine handsome fellow I was becoming. Little did I know what was in store for me by the end of the month.

I had by now learnt that the roads around us were quite busy and that I had to listen very carefully before crossing them. During my various excursions I was to discover that the village was not very large.

At the end where the sun set there was a small road bridge over the Piddle Brook. Going towards where the sun rose, the houses started on both sides of the road. There was a church on the left, more houses including an old black and white one on the right, then a small village green where the road forked. The main road bore through the village to the left, and there was a narrow lane with more houses to the right. The farm belonging the farmer and his wife lay between these two roads. Further up the main road were a few more houses ending at The Elms, a black and white house with another farmyard at the rear which was used mostly as stables and storage, but proved to be a good spot for hunting. Up the narrow lane there were several more houses and another working farm with cows in the sheds, hay in a Dutch barn, straw in another barn, cattle food in sacks and an abundance of wildlife jealously guarded by Ginger, for this was his home.

It was towards the end of the month that Rod packed me back into the cardboard box and took me to the vet's. Once again I was terrified that he was taking me back to the tithe barn, but I soon recognised the smells peculiar to the surgery, and I wondered what was about to happen. I heard Rod talking to someone and then leave. My box was carried into another room and opened. A woman took me out and deposited me in a cage with no food or water. By now I was trembling with fear, but all I could do was sit and wait, occasionally calling out to attract attention. A dog was whining close by, but there was no sound of other cats.

Eventually the woman returned, took me out of the cage and carried me into a room with a bright shiny table, beside which stood a man in a green dress-like garment. There was a horrible smell I had not come across before, something like disinfectant. The woman held me down on the table while the man cut the hair off one of my front legs with some sort of machine. Then he picked up something else and stuck it into my leg.

Suddenly I began to feel hot and sleepy, and that was the last I remember before waking up with a terrible headache, a peculiar taste in my mouth, a very sore feeling between my back legs and watering eyes. I didn't know what they had done to me, only that I felt awful.

I spent a few more hours in the cage, occasionally drinking a little water to try to get rid of the nasty taste in my mouth, before a girl put me back into my cardboard box and Rod came to collect me.

When we got home I was placed in my basket in front of the log-burning stove in the lounge and, despite my discomfort, I soon fell asleep. I was woken some time later and taken into the kitchen for a light snack, before being carried back into the lounge where I stayed for the rest of the evening.

I felt somewhat better the next day and, although it was bitterly cold outside, I managed to squeeze my sore body through the cat flap and took myself for a walk around the wilderness. It wasn't long before I chanced upon an unwary vole, which I swiftly despatched and devoured, and that made me feel much better. How could I understand what had been done to me? It was only later that the full realisation of what had happened on that fateful day dawned on me, and that, handsome as I was, I would never be able to father my own children.

As the days passed the fur on my leg began to grow back and my wound healed nicely so that, as autumn turned to winter, I became fully mobile again.

Sammy

CHAPTER THREE

FIRST WINTER

November started very cold, wet and windy. So I spent little time outside, preferring the warmth beside the log-burner and all the comforts of home.

One Saturday preparations began for a dinner party to celebrate Diane's birthday. I wandered in and out of the kitchen, picking up some interesting and tempting new food smells. Being an opportunist I only had to bide my time before seizing my chance. It came while backs were turned. I leapt onto the surface of the breakfast bar, a forbidden area, and sampled a few prawns from one of several dishes, before moving on to enjoy the cream on the top of a pudding, delicious and too good to leave.

It was while I was manoeuvring to examine other offerings that disaster struck. I am normally very spatially aware, but on this occasion I managed to get one of my back feet into the dish of prawns. When I tried to extract it, the dish slipped, toppled over and hit the floor, smashing into pieces. Diane turned, saw me and shouted. With the noise of the breaking glass and the shout from Diane, I lost my natural reserve, panicked, and headed for the floor. A chocolate trifle covered in cream just happened to be in front of me, and not realising that my back paw and the surface were now slippery from the prawns, I tried to leap over it. Disaster struck again, my rear paws lost purchase and the leap failed to get the required elevation, but I did manage to generate considerable propulsion. The result was an uncontrolled skid with back feet flailing for purchase and a collision with the bowl of trifle, which joined the prawns on the floor. My nearest exit was into the hall, so I leapt to the floor, ran upstairs and hid under a bed. Again my escape was ill-judged because my jump to the floor landed me in the spilt trifle, and I left a dreadful mess of chocolate and cream footprints behind me. While I was taking a great deal of pleasure in washing the chocolate, cream and prawn mixture from my paws, I heard Diane sobbing downstairs and realised that at that moment I was not the most popular cat in the village.

Sometime later a now calm Diane came looking for me and pulled me gently from under the bed. Far from being annoyed, she picked me up, cuddled me and told me not to worry because it was her fault for not understanding me properly. She carried me downstairs, took me into the utility room, and there on the floor was a small bowl of prawns as a treat for me. That evening after the children had gone to bed several strangers arrived, and I was paraded before them and much admired. I was then taken to my basket in the utility room before they sat down to supper.

Later that evening I woke up to the sound of bangs and flashes from outside in the garden, accompanied by laughter and talking. I found the noise was quite frightening and hid in the corner until the commotion ended. There was some talk of fireworks and bonfire night. Things improved much later when the visitors departed, the clearing away and washing up were completed, a few tasty morsels were placed on a saucer for my supper, and peace and quiet returned to my household.

At the end of that month, Rod disappeared on an overseas business trip to a place I heard them call "The Far East". The house was very quiet in the evenings without him, and I missed being able to snuggle up on his lap. I tried curling up in his chair, which still had his comforting smell, but it lacked his warmth, so I decided to approach Diane. She had a more comfortable lap than Rod, and I think she was missing him as well, so in a way we comforted each other.

It was during the time Rod was away that I awoke one morning to see that someone seemed to have painted the garden white! The lawn was white, the trees white, and the hedge white; in fact the outside world appeared to be almost in black and white. When the cat flap was opened I ventured outside and my paws sank into the white stuff covering the ground. I tried to walk, only to find that whatever it was came halfway up my legs and stuck to my fur coat. I tried running and almost fell over, and then I heard the children laughing at me. Now, I do not consider myself to be a figure of fun, so I slowed down and walked in as dignified a manner as possible along the patio, over the lawn and through the hedge into the wilderness. It was not so bad in here, although some of the white stuff had settled on the long grass and tended to fall on me as I passed. I assumed that this area had been better sheltered and that more of whatever it was had blown into our own garden.

There were tracks from small rodents, and by the pond signs of where birds had been trying to drink from the frozen water. I assumed that most of the other animals had retreated to their nests or dens to keep out of the cold.

However, undaunted and now beginning to master the art of walking through the stuff rather than trying to step over it, I moved to a house on the other side of the road where I had spotted a table in the garden on which they put out food for the birds. Birds, being generally messy eaters, often spilt bread and nuts onto the ground, and I had noticed in the past that this sometimes attracted field mice and other small animals. There was a flower bed to one side where I hid under a bush, thinking that I would just give it a few minutes before returning home. To my surprise a sparrow landed on the bush, and it was the simplest task to spring out and catch him. I made short work of tearing the feathers off him, and he made a more than adequate breakfast. To prove that I was not a figure of fun, I carefully picked up his head, retraced my steps home and presented my trophy to my family who were just finishing their breakfast. Once again I received a mixed reception. Diane picked it up in a piece of paper and put it into a bin, but Chris thought I was very clever, while Carolyn thought I shouldn't kill birds. How could I ever get it right?

The snow, for that is what I heard the children say it was, eventually melted and several weeks passed until, amidst much excitement from Diane and the children, Rod returned laden with presents for everyone - including a clockwork mouse for me. The children found it almost as exciting as I did, winding it up, putting it down for me to chase, and watching me catch it, then I would let it go and chase it again accompanied by their squeals of excitement. Rod had brought Carolyn a furry toy, which I heard them say was a panda, made in China from rabbit fur. She was ecstatic, and carried it everywhere with her. I failed to understand how I could be so wrong in bringing mice and birds home, yet Rod could arrive with a trophy made of rabbit and not be criticised! What he did not know at the time was that he had introduced Carolyn to fur as a comforter. From that moment on until she was grown up she was always to take a piece of fur to bed with her, and over the years he had to buy numerous replacement pandas for the ones that were worn out.

Although the snow had gone, the last days of November stayed very cold with frost, fog and bitter winds. As we entered my first December the weather took a turn for the better, and I was able to go out more frequently and resume my hunting activities. I was by now ready to extend the range of my explorations once again, and one day in early December while everybody was out, I made my first sortie in the direction of the sunset, travelling behind the big black and white house called The Old Rectory and then past the back gardens of two bungalows. Just beyond these I heard the sound of running water and, squeezing through some brambles, came upon the Piddle Brook for the first time. This stream ran under a small road bridge and formed a boundary on that side of the village.

I discovered on subsequent visits that the water level in the brook could vary considerably from day to day depending on rainfall or snow melting; on one day it would be calm, quiet and just trickling along, on another it would be swift, full and dangerous. On that particular day the stream flowed swiftly and the water level was almost to the top of the banks. As I approached, a moorhen scuttled away from the edge and paddled swiftly to the other side. I stood watching the muddy water and decided that I should not get too close. Rather than approach the road over the bridge, from which came the sound of occasional traffic, I turned to the left and followed the bank of the stream towards some open fields where cattle were grazing. The side of the brook was very overgrown. Here and there were willow trees, and about a hundred yards away a small copse and a hedge dividing the fields ran back in the direction of the village where I could see a few houses in the distance. There were signs of various burrowing animals, and at one point I saw a quite large greyish-coloured creature with a white bobtail rush into one of the holes. Fascinated, I sank to the ground and crawled slowly forward with my belly to the ground. The rabbit warren by the hedge, for that is what it was, was some way back from the brook. I could smell the rabbits and see their little round droppings on the ground. I found a large tuft of grass a few yards downwind from the entrance to the warren, and well concealed, I crouched silently.

It wasn't long before I heard movement from the underground tunnel and a small head appeared. I had by now learnt the secret of patience, so I waited until this obvious youngster, having sniffed the air, stood up on his hind legs, looked around and, satisfied that the coast was clear, hopped out and began busily munching grass. A few moments later a much larger rabbit that I assumed was his mother emerged, followed by a group of chattering rabbit children who immediately stopped their hubbub and put their heads down to enjoy the grass.

I kept still, knowing instinctively that sooner or later their appetites would bring them towards me. Sure enough, after about five minutes, one of the little fellows hopped away from the safety of his burrow and family, and came to within a few feet of me. Drawing my hind legs under me I sprang. He reacted quickly, swiftly turning towards the others as I left the ground, but he was not quick enough. I simply extended my left paw to the side before landing and caught his hindquarters with my claws, spinning him to the ground. I heard him pant and squeal and was aware of the others bolting for their home. My little fellow regained his feet and, with eyes bulging, made another dash to follow them. But I was not to be thwarted. Here was the biggest catch of my life so far, so reeling round I grabbed him again with my claws and, seizing the back of his neck between my teeth, held on tight while he struggled and kicked. Eventually he quietened down, and I shook him vigorously from side to side until I felt his neck break and his struggles ceased.

I was a comparatively long way from home, but I was determined to exhibit my latest trophy to my family so I laid him on the ground while I took a short rest. At that moment two things happened: first, the rain which had been threatening all day began to fall, and within moments became a downpour. Secondly, seemingly from nowhere, a large black carrion crow appeared, his purple-black feathers glistening with the rain and his beady eyes staring at me. He squawked and hopped nearer to my rabbit. I hissed, raised my tail and hackles, and moved towards him. He squawked again and seemed to jump and flap his wings at the same time, leaving the ground and giving my back a sharp peck. I turned and saw that he was now beside the rabbit, pecking at its eyes. Then, probably drawn by the noise of its mate, another of the vicious birds drifted to the ground. What was a young cat to do? Certainly not give up without a fight so, gathering myself together again, I circled behind the first of the invaders, only to be set upon by the wings and claws of the other one.

The birds were both bigger than me and particularly vicious so, not wanting to sustain any more injuries, I reluctantly moved a few feet back and watched in dismay as they were joined by even more of their kind, all of whom proceeded to tear my rabbit to pieces.

By now I was soaking wet, nursing a few scratches and bruises from the claws and wings of the crows, dejected because of my loss, disorientated and unsure which direction to take to get home. The rain was turning to sleet and I could see no more than a few feet, the crows were arguing and squawking over the rabbit, and I could just hear the sound of the brook in the distance. Should I head towards this, pick up my own scent and retrace my steps home, or would it be quicker to turn my back on the sound and try to head in the direction of the houses I had seen earlier? I thought that the brook might be dangerous in those conditions so set off across the field. The noises of the birds and the stream slowly faded and, knowing that I must be getting nearer to home and warmth, my confidence began to rise.

It was then that I began to sense danger. The smell of cattle had been gradually getting stronger and I could hear the sound of numerous animals chewing not far away. Suddenly, a huge creature emerged out of the downpour with steam pouring from its nostrils. I swerved away from it, heard it snort and stamp a foot. Then another snort came from just in front of me and yet another from my left-hand side. I realised in near panic that somehow I had managed to get into the middle of the herd of cows. There was only one thing to be done, so plucking up my courage I ran and ran and ran as fast as I could until the bovine sounds receded into the distance. Not long afterwards I came to a gap in a hedge where, beside a trough of water, the ground had been churned into mud by the cattle. The hoof marks were full of water, but by now all I wanted was to be home, dry and safe so I plunged forward through the disgusting wet, cold, dirty and smelly quagmire, and a few moments later found myself by the fence no more than a few minutes from home.

I ran across our garden, and leapt through the cat flap into the warmth of home. No one was in, so I quickly went into the lounge, sat in front of the log-burner for a while to warm up and dry out, and then curled up in the armchair for a well-earned rest. I awoke sometime later when the family returned, and once again found myself unpopular - something to do with mud in the utility room, on the carpet and all over the chair. I was bundled into the kitchen, put onto an old towel and had to suffer the indignity of being brushed and combed. I must confess that I felt much cleaner afterwards, but nevertheless gave myself a good wash all over to take away the human smell. It is another thing I have learnt: while it is very nice to have all the attention from my family, every time they handle me I have to wash off their smells which, although sometimes quite pleasant, can be detected by my prey.

Just before the middle of the month Carolyn had a birthday party. There was much excitement that day as preparations were made and the table in the dining room laid with food, with the door kept firmly closed to prevent any further accidents! I went out for my usual prowl around my territory but by now the small rodents seemed scarce. Either I had scared them away or they were asleep for the winter. I met Daisy over at the barn, but she didn't seem so friendly. I was by now bigger than her, and I think she was getting nervous about my size and confidence. We spent some time waiting patiently for signs of life but nothing emerged so, feeling cold, I returned home for a quiet sleep. Alas, it was not to be. Carolyn's friends started arriving and she was keen to show me off, so I found myself being passed from one person to another. Some of them admired me greatly and others were a bit rough, but I knew I should be patient and put up with it. They soon tired of me and started playing noisy games so, for peace and quiet, I hid beneath one of the beds and they forgot about me. When I awoke all was quiet again as the children had all gone home, so I returned to my favourite lap in the lounge, happy that normality had returned to the household.

The following day the most extraordinary thing happened. Rod brought a tree into the lounge and he and Diane started putting twinkling lights, shiny balls and stuff they called tinsel on to it. It stood in the corner of the room and was unlike any tree I had found on my travels; it gave off a perfumed smell that was quite pleasant, and the decorations were very pretty. I wasn't sure if it was a new toy for my benefit or something to decorate their house. Anyway, it looked to have plenty of entertainment value so when they were out of the room I approached, crawled underneath and managed to climb onto one of the lower branches. I was reaching for one of the shiny balls when the tree moved, and I realised that unlike the trees outside this one was not firmly rooted in the ground. So very carefully I edged backwards towards the trunk, gently eased myself to the ground and returned to the armchair as if nothing had happened. By now Rod and Diane were in the hall and dining room putting up all sorts of decorations, so it was some time before they came into the lounge and noticed the peculiar angle at which the tree was standing. I watched them through one half-open eye, pretending that I was asleep. No one suspected that the drunken tilt was my fault! Rod crawled under the tree and made some adjustments while Diane returned it to an upright position. After a few minutes and some complaints about pine needles down his collar, he emerged satisfied that the tree was now stable.

I decided against another attempt to climb into the tree, but I did manage to remove one of the shiny balls and chase it around the lounge. It had a lump at one end that made it move in an irregular way when I pushed it with my paw, sometimes going straight and sometimes jumping to one side or the other. I became more and more excited by this strange phenomenon and kept hitting it harder and harder and chasing faster and faster after it – fun, but not as good as a mouse! Eventually I tired of the ball, pushed it under the tree and returned to the chair for a sleep.

Over the next few days, various gift-wrapped parcels were placed under the tree amidst much excitement from the children. I found these quite intriguing and on several occasions tried to investigate their contents, but I only succeeded in removing a couple of fancy bows and name tags, and slightly tearing the wrapping on one of them. This caused another rumpus, and I was scolded again and warned to keep away.

Excitement built up over the following days, heightened on Christmas Eve by the arrival of Diane's mum and dad, Reg and Doris, who it transpired were going to stay with us for the Christmas holiday. They arrived with even more presents which they added to the pile under the tree. These were also prodded, poked and shaken by the children who couldn't wait to find out what was inside them. Excitement continued to build as the day went on, other relations and friends called in and presents were exchanged. They took the opportunity of showing me off to everyone who arrived and, since I was on my best behaviour and had once again undergone the ordeal of being brushed and combed, I was much admired by all comers.

It didn't take me long to realise that Diane's father didn't like me. He apparently had a dislike of all cats and I heard him saying that they were always doing their business in his garden and digging up his seedlings. Since I didn't even know where his garden was, I took this as an unwarranted accusation and so I set out to change his attitude towards me. With this in mind I would wait in the armchair until he settled in the place he had established at the end of the sofa, and then I would jump down, amble across and rub myself up against his leg before jumping onto his lap and curling up. It didn't matter to me whether he was trying to read his newspaper, watch television, talk or drink his tea, as soon as he settled I was there. At first he objected and pushed me down, but I persisted, and eventually he gave up and let me stay saying: "Why is it that cats go to the one person who doesn't like them?" I think that by the time they left after Christmas he had decided I wasn't so bad after all.

That evening the children were full of excitement and would not go to sleep. Chris kept coming downstairs and enquiring about someone called Father Christmas. He and Carolyn had left a glass of whisky and a mince pie by the log-burner for him as well as a carrot for his reindeer. About midnight, when the children were sound asleep, pillowcases full of parcels were carried quietly into their rooms, and then Rod did a very strange thing. He opened the door of the log-burner which had not been alight that day, pulled out some of the logs that had been laid in there and scattered them on the hearth and carpet.

He then gathered a bit of soot from inside and dropped this on the carpet between the logs. Then laughing as Diane, Reg and Doris watched, he drank the whisky, ate the mince pie and nibbled the side out of the carrot. I was puzzled but felt sure that he must know what he was doing.

Shortly after that everyone retired for the night, leaving me curled up in my own bed. Very early the next morning, before daybreak, I heard noises from the children's rooms and people creeping around upstairs. This was most unusual and I wondered what was going on. A bit later Rod came down, stroked my ears and said: "Happy Christmas Sam, I expect you wonder what it's all about." He then made cups of tea and carried those upstairs, leaving the kitchen door open and calling me to follow.

The children were in the main bedroom showing off an assort-ment of toys, games, chocolate and fruit that they seemed to think had been brought by this fellow Father Christmas. Rod sent them downstairs on some pretext and they came running back up saying that Father Christmas had made an awful mess in the lounge when he came down the chimney, but that he had eaten the mince pie and drunk the whisky. I knew better!

What an exciting day it was. The table in the dining room was laid, a great big turkey put into the oven, vegetables prepared, a pudding put into a pan to steam, and the children rushed in and out with new toys. About mid-day, Rod's parents arrived with even more presents, and the first round of drinks was served. There was a lovely smell emanating from the kitchen, and I felt sure that I was going to be allowed to share in their feast. At about two o'clock in the afternoon they carved the turkey and served up lunch in the dining room, leaving me a bowl of the most succulent warm meat which I devoured with relish. Satisfied, I returned to the armchair and listened to the excited talk from the dining room. When they had finished they came back into the lounge to drink coffee and something called port, before Rod distributed the presents from under the tree. There was even one for me, containing a ball with a rattle inside, and some of my favourite Munchies. Despite the noise and excitement, I decided that Christmas Day was pretty good.

The adults fell asleep that afternoon and, because it was cold and wet outside, I curled up on Reg's lap and had a contented sleep myself. That evening they sat down for a cold supper before Rod's parents left, and everyone went to bed early.

Celebrations carried on the next day with the arrival of Rod's teenage children, Therese and Dominic, and yet more presents were distributed and another sumptuous lunch provided. They got on very well with Carolyn and Chris, and everyone had a good time. Again I was given turkey with my dinner, so I didn't feel the need to get cold and wet hunting outside. Instead, I settled for the comfort of one lap or another.

The days passed and, although it seemed like just another day to me, New Year was celebrated by the popping of champagne corks at midnight.

Reg and Doris departed on New Year's Day and the house gradually returned to normality. Rod and Diane went back to work, and a few days later the Christmas tree was removed from the lounge, the decorations and lights packed into boxes, and everything put up into the loft. I was not to know it at that time, but a momentous year lay ahead.

Toby

CHAPTER FOUR

A LEGEND IS BORN

January was cold and wet. During the week the adults were at work and the children at school, so I was left to my own devices during the daytime. When it was raining I stayed inside keeping warm and dry, but on the better days I started to explore further field. The mice in the barn were now few and far between and there was little else for me to catch in the wilderness behind our house, so one day in the middle of January I decided to venture into the barn up the lane, near the house where Ginger lived.

With great caution and stealth I approached the barn from a gate by the road. There were stacks of straw and hay, a tractor and trailer were parked in the middle of the farmyard and ruts full of ice led into the barn. I took my time, keeping a constant lookout for Ginger in the knowledge that I was now deep into his territory. But seeing no sign of him, I picked my way across the icy ruts and jumped up onto the bales of straw. I could smell mice and saw signs of their droppings everywhere so knew that the hunting would be better here. Sensing no danger and confident that I was unseen, I leapt onto one of the higher bales and came face to face with the village bully! I suppose it was inevitable that my growing confidence would eventually lead me into trouble. Fortunately he decided to put on a display of hostility, rather than make an instant attack. This gave me the few moments I needed to gather myself together. Ginger had his hackles raised and was snarling and spitting at me. I circled round him and realised that he was slightly larger than me, and that although my only fight had been with the vicious crows, I was now going to have to use all my cunning and guile to get away alive. Ginger sprang at me and I rolled sideways, lashing out with my front claws as he passed over me, and catching him hard in the abdomen. He squealed and returned to the attack. Our heads and mouths met, biting, clawing and scratching, each of us trying to inflict as much damage as possible to the other.

I felt his teeth dig into the side of my face and blood begin to flow. I went for his eyes with my front claws while ripping at his belly with my back feet. He squealed, and backed off. We circled each other and he came in again claws scratching across my nose, before I ducked and somehow managed to throw my weight against him, making him fall backwards. Seizing my chance, I went for his throat and, before he could get up, grabbed him and shook as hard as I could. He squealed and screamed and I shook and shook, at the same time digging at him with my back claws. Realising that he was now at my mercy, I let go and stood over him. He quietened down and lay on his back in submission, so I backed away, and watched him slink down the bales and off towards the farmhouse.

My first battle was won, but I was bleeding from the bite on my cheek and from numerous scratches on my nose and ears, to say nothing of the ones hidden under the fur on my body. As the excitement diminished, the pain began. Should I go home, or take advantage of my victory and continue my hunt? I flopped down and licked my wounds while I got my breath back, and then lay a while to see if any small rodents would come out after all the noise we had been making. Keeping a watchful eye out for Ginger, I waited.

It was some time before I saw the first movements on the bales below, as several mice emerged and started scratching in one of them for wheat left by the harvesting machine. When they were fully engrossed in filling their stomachs, I pounced and killed the largest one. The others scattered, allowing me to settle down for a tasty lunch. I did get one glimpse of Ginger, watching me from a window in the house, but he must have decided that he had had enough. My injuries were still hurting and I was beginning to stiffen up so I decided to make my way home. Carefully, I climbed down, picked my way through the icy ruts back to the road and limped off. As I crawled through the cat flap I felt the bruises and scratches on my body, and wondered how much damage I had really done to Ginger. Did he feel as sore as I did?

I curled up in my basket and started to clean myself. The worst pain came from the bite in my cheek, which had bled quite a bit and was now oozing a clear liquid. Despite the pain I fell asleep. I was woken up by the return of Diane and the children. They showed a great deal of concern when they saw me, so I must have looked as bad as I felt. When Rod came home, they put me by the sink in the kitchen and bathed my ears, nose and face with some horrible smelling stuff that made my wounds sting, telling me that it would make me better.

The next day the scratches on my face and body did seem to be better but I had a terrible pain in my face, which was swollen where I had been bitten. By evening, when Diane came home, I felt very unwell and could barely open my mouth to eat or drink. She packed me into the travelling box, loaded me into the car and took me to the vet's. After a long wait in the smelly waiting room alongside a variety of other cats and a few dogs, I was taken into the surgery where the vet examined my face. Diane explained that a cat had bitten me and he agreed that it looked as though I had been in a fight, so he gave me an injection. The pain was considerable for the rest of that evening, and I found it difficult to eat, drink or sleep. The following morning it was slightly less painful, but Diane held me while Rod forced a pill down my throat.

It was time to keep my eye on my newly-won territory, so I made my way up the lane to the scene of my fight with Ginger. I was cautiously approaching the farmyard when Daisy came running after me. "Sam," she meowed, "it's all over the village that you beat Ginger. Does he look as bad as you? You look more like the loser than the winner they say you are!"

I raised my tail, lifted my aching head into a proud position and invited her to come with me to see my new hunting ground. "Don't worry," I said. "I'll look after you. Ginger won't dare do anything." So we sauntered into what had been forbidden territory and made ourselves comfortable among the bales in the barn. The only signs of life were two sheepdogs that barked briefly at us before wandering away.

We had caught a couple of mice and were just about to leave when we heard the cat flap at the house and Ginger came slowly round the corner. All pain forgotten, I sprang from my bale and raced towards him. Daisy let out a screech; he spotted me, turned tail and bolted back into the house through the cat flap. "There you are Daisy, do you want any further proof of who is top cat now?" I enquired. In response she came and rubbed up against me saying, "I always knew you were special, Sammy. You've proved it to all of us now - but please don't turn into a bully like Ginger." I reassured her that all I had done was to teach him a lesson and that I would do the same to any other cat that tried to take over our territory. Over the next few days, as my wounds gradually healed, several other cats cautiously approached me to offer their friendship and congratulations. I began to realise that my victory over Ginger had made me the hero of the village.

As the days passed, Rod and Diane kept forcing pills down my throat until my wounds healed. I was left with a small scar on my nose and a nick in my ear where it had been torn in the fight; I believe that these battle scars added distinction to my handsome features.

It was now February, and the days got longer as the sun rose a little earlier and set a little later each day. There was often a bitter north wind, but in sheltered places the sun gave more warmth. We had another smattering of snow in the middle of the month and, when that had gone, the first flowers started to show in the flower beds and hedgerows. Spring was on the way. The birds began to sing again and to collect twigs and moss to make their nests. It may seem unkind, but it was the beginning of a new hunting season for me, stalking unwary birds sometimes so intent on catching the early morning worms or gathering nesting material that they never knew what hit them. Death was quick and merciful; after all, they had been caught by a legend!

My reputation had spread throughout the area and all the other cats seemed to respect my superiority. I suppose this gave me greater confidence, and I now strode through the village in the knowledge that this was my domain. Even the dogs treated me with respect. They sometimes barked as I passed by, but never ventured further than their own front gates.

Sometimes I saw Ginger. He would raise his hackles and swish his tail in anger but never approach me, just slink away glancing over his shoulder to make sure I wasn't following. Confident in my superiority, I put all thoughts of danger from my mind: this was almost my undoing.

What I had failed to realise was that Ginger was not only older and more experienced than me, I had usurped his territory and he was not going to give in as easily as I had thought. His behaviour was all part of his plan to lead me into a false sense of security, and in that he succeeded beyond his wildest dreams. Daily I went into the barn, lay on my favourite bale of straw and waited for the mice. The hunting was good, my colouring camouflaging me almost perfectly in the straw and shadows. All I had to do was keep still, be patient and eventually some foolish mouse would appear. It was a routine that I fell easily into, unaware that I was being watched.

Several weeks later, I sprang onto what I now considered to be my personal bale and lay down to await my prey. Unbeknown to me, Ginger had arrived sometime earlier and approached from the other side of the barn so that I would not pick up his scent. He had waited for a day when the strong northerly wind blew my scent towards him. In that way he would know of my arrival without having to show himself, and the noise of the wind would cover any sound he might make in approaching me. Oh yes, he was smart and cunning. It is easy to be wise in hindsight and I made a mistake I was never to make again. I hadn't checked above me because my concentration was on the bales below and I had walked straight into Ginger's ambush. He was hiding above and behind me, and the first I knew about it was when he dropped some ten feet straight onto my back with claws extended. The first assault almost winded me. My saving grace was that he had not allowed for the instability of the bale on which I was lying. Under the force of his fall, it toppled, sending us both flying through the air. Although his initial attack had been one hundred percent successful and he had driven his claws into my back, his luck ran out when the bale fell. Still locked together by his claws, we crashed onto the floor below with Ginger underneath.

Fortunately for me Ginger's body acted as a cushion, taking some of the shock out of the impact. He was less fortunate. Not only did he have the wind knocked out of him by his back hitting the solid, frozen surface of the floor, but my not inconsiderable weight compressed his body to such an extent that I heard his breath whoosh out and his ribs crack. His claws were still embedded in my back but, ignoring the pain, I rolled to one side, separating myself from him. He could barely move, but I knew that this had to be the final conflict so I set about him with claws and teeth, determined to finish him for good. I live in a savage world where only the strong survive, and I have no doubt that, but for the insecurity of that bale, it would have been I who was to die that day. I'm not proud of what followed, but finally I stood back and surveyed the wreck of what had once been a dominant male. I had scratched and torn at him relentlessly, he was covered in his own blood and totally unable to defend himself, but I hadn't the heart to finish him. I stood foursquare over him, listening to his rasping breath and seeing an appeal for mercy in his eyes. This I offered if he promised to leave all the other cats alone, agreed that all territory would be controlled by me, and guaranteed to stay away from me forever more. He had little option but to accept, and with that I moved back and allowed him to hobble away. I knew how lucky I had been, for although I had some scratches on my back, I was otherwise unmarked. How different the outcome would have been had we crashed to the floor with him on top of me.

The weeks passed and spring came with the warming sun and blossom bursting on the trees. The swallows returned and the house martins started nesting in the eaves of the house. I was woken each morning by a cacophony of birdsong, blackbird and song thrush, sparrows twittering, pigeons cooing and all the birds of the hedgerow welcoming the new day. At the end of April, I heard a cuckoo for the first time, and I wondered what sort of magical bird could make such an unusual sound.

Daily I patrolled my territory, acknowledging other cats as I passed and supplementing my ration of tinned food with fresh-caught rodents.

I was now almost one year old and must have been one of the most contented cats on earth, for this was surely feline paradise.

The Malvern Hills

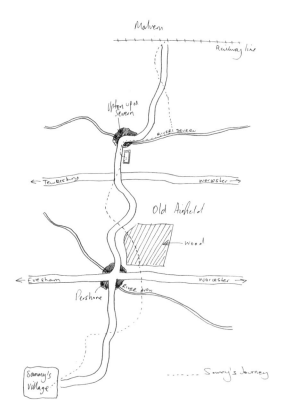

CHAPTER FIVE

THE ADVENTURE

Rod and Diane were now content to let me come and go as I pleased. The nights were drawing out and the cat flap was left permanently open. The litter tray had disappeared but fresh water and tinned food was put down for me morning and night. I spent less and less time indoors now that the weather was improving, but I made sure that I got home in time for my dinner. The evenings I passed with the family, usually curled up on Rod's lap until bedtime when they would open the front door and put me outside. That is apart from the nights when it was raining, when they would leave me in the utility room, but I could still go out through the cat flap when I wanted.

It must have been sometime in early May when, one Friday afternoon, a man came to do something to one of the televisions. I watched him arrive in a van and Diane let him in. I followed and observed him taking the back off the set and working on the inside. Getting bored, I wandered outside and decided to inspect his van. Jumping into the back, I found boxes of tools, another television, a white sheet and a packet of sandwiches which he must have opened for his lunch. They gave off the lovely aroma of salmon so I proceeded to eat my fill. Feeling satisfied, I curled up on the white sheet and fell into a deep, contented sleep.

The next thing I was aware of was the slamming of the rear door of the van. The driver got into the cab and started the engine. I realised instantly that he had been unaware of me and that I was now trapped. I meowed and scratched at the back door but to no avail because the noise of the tyres on the road and the engine drowned out any sounds I made. There was nothing for it but to wait and see what happened next.

I don't know how long we drove for but it was quite a while before the van stopped, and I heard the driver get out and talk to someone before coming round to the back and opening the door. To avoid detection, I hid behind the television until I heard him wander off. Creeping forward, I saw that we were in a yard surrounded by buildings except where a double gate led to the outside world, and through which I could see houses and the outskirts of a town (Sammy had arrived at Malvern). I was lost and frightened, and I didn't know what to do.

By now it was mid-afternoon. I could see the sun overhead and black clouds rolling in over large, dark hills that stood above the town. I decided to make a move before the sun set so jumped down from the van and ran towards the gates. Traffic was flashing past so I kept to the pavement rather than get knocked over. I had walked about a hundred yards when I saw a small gate leading into the front garden of a house. I entered unobserved, and hid under a bush to gather my wits. Where was I, and how was I going to find my way home? I told myself not to panic and slowly reason came to me. On my evening hunt across the fields of my home village, I had often watched the sun go down over distant hills. Were these the same hills that stood above the town where I now found myself? Surely they must be! In that case I must walk away from the setting sun and towards the rising sun to find my home. Would any other cat have been clever enough to come to this conclusion, I wondered? Come what may, I must get home and start before sunset.

Keeping the hills behind me, I scrambled through a hedge into the next garden and then crossed over several others, before being confronted by an angry dog and having to beat a hasty retreat over a wall into the street again. I walked down the pavement and noticed that on the other side of the road there was some open ground and a few trees. I was waiting for a gap in the traffic before making a dash for it when the heavens opened and the rain poured down. Passing cars covered me with spray, and I suddenly felt cold, wet, lonely and frightened. The traffic eased for a moment, and I ran across to the grass on the other side of the road and hurried away from the noisy road.

There were signs of rabbits, but for once I ignored them and pressed on, past children playing with a ball and people walking dogs on a large area of open land. I reached the other side of the field and was confronted by an embankment leading down to some steel rails. I was about to go down the bank when a huge engine thundered past towing some trucks. I leapt back in terror and realised that I could not progress in that direction, so I followed the embankment back to the road. Here I found a bridge over the strange rails; I crossed this without difficulty and turned into a quieter road. There was less traffic here but I felt it would be safer to progress through the gardens of the houses, rather than use the pavement beside the road.

I won't dwell on the details of the terrifying journey through the town. Suffice to say it was noisy, smelly, and busy with cars, people, dogs and untold danger. I crossed numerous roads and cut through various gardens. After about two hours the houses became further apart, and at last and with relief, I reached open countryside.

The rain had now stopped, but I must have presented a sorry sight with my mud-spattered, bedraggled coat. I stopped for a short rest and looked back at the hills looming behind me to make sure I was still moving in the right direction. Evening was creeping on and I was beginning to feel the first pangs of hunger. I had taken a drink from a puddle I passed, but where was I to find food? I was in the countryside so surely there must be a farm somewhere with a supply of tasty mice to keep me going! I could hear cattle mooing in the distance, so I made my way in their direction and soon saw a farmyard. The farmer was driving the cows into a field. While he was busy, I slipped into the farmyard and found a barn with bales of straw, climbed up onto them and settled down. My first priority was to wash and clean myself to get the smell of the town out of my coat. I then fell into an exhausted sleep, troubled only by dreams of lorries and cars rushing towards me.

When I awoke, night had fallen. Although I felt refreshed, my stomach was rumbling with hunger. I could see light coming from the farmhouse so I set off in that direction in search of food. As I approached the back of the house, I picked up the smell of food and was amazed to find a dish of cat food by the back door. I realised that the farmer must have cats of his own and had put out their evening meal. Keeping a wary eye out for them, I devoured all that was in the dish then returned to the barn and again fell into a deep sleep. As the sun rose I was woken up by the noise of mice scampering below. Breakfast! I quickly despatched and feasted on the plumpest of them, drank from a puddle and set off towards the sunrise.

I realised that if I was ever to find my way home I must keep moving and wherever possible avoid roads and houses, where the greatest danger lay. With this in mind I crossed fields and hedges, taking detours to avoid ditches filled with water, but always keeping the sombre hills behind me. I saw all sorts of wildlife, and occasionally farmers in the distance, some with dogs tending their sheep, others on tractors doing various jobs in the fields. I kept well away from all of them, slinking past in the long grass and creeping through the hedges. It would have been easy to be distracted by the voles and birds, but my determination kept me going and I began to feel more confident that I would soon be home.

The few roads I came across were quiet and I had no difficulty in crossing them, but by midday I was getting tired. I wasn't used to all this walking and I was beginning to wonder just how far I had to go. I checked behind me once again and, although the hills seemed much further away, they still looked a great deal larger than they had from home. Perhaps I was half way, perhaps not.

Shortly after this I crossed another busy road and heard the sound of water. Scrambling down a steep bank, I was confronted by the largest river I had ever seen (Sammy had reached the River Severn). The current was flowing fast and I could see no way of getting across. What was I to do? As I sat pondering the problem, a small rabbit emerged from the undergrowth just to my left. I sprang, caught and killed him, and had an excellent lunch. Rather than worry too much about my problem, I lay down in the warm sunshine and fell into a contented sleep.

Afternoon turned to evening as I slept. It was dark when I awoke, and much cooler. The sky to my left was lit up by the lights of a large town (Worcester). Should I go in that direction or the other way? Having experienced the horrors of a town the day before, I opted to go downstream, away from the town, but to wait until daylight before making a start.

After another night's sleep I felt much better, so I breakfasted off the remains of the rabbit, took a drink from the river's edge and set off keeping it to my left. The riverbank was level and quiet, there were no roads to cross and no human activity. I came across the occasional stream flowing down to the river but always there were small gateways with bridges that must have been used by farmers. By crossing these I progressed steadily, but I still could not see any way of getting over the big river.

Late in the afternoon I heard the sound of traffic to my right, and I realised that the road was now quite close to the river; perhaps it crossed it somewhere ahead? I picked up my pace and crossed the back garden of a large house. This led into a field with strange houses on wheels which all seemed to be empty. I left these behind and squeezed through a hedge into another field from where I could see a town ahead (Upton upon Severn). And, more important, the bridge I had hoped for existed. I lay down and watched cars crossing in both directions. It was very busy so I felt that it would be wise to wait. As the sun set over the distant hills, the traffic slackened and it was time to cross. There was a pavement protected from the traffic by a metal barrier so, summoning all my courage, I made a dash for it and in a few moments was safely on the other side. I walked a little further until across the road I saw more houses on wheels. Several were in darkness, but a few had lights on and people were moving around inside. I wanted to investigate before darkness fell completely.

So I crossed the road, went through a gate and approached the nearest house on wheels with a light inside. The delicious smell of fish being cooked wafted through the half-open door. It was simply irresistible so I climbed onto a little step, meowed and put my head through the door. Inside, an elderly lady stood by a cooker and a man sat watching television. I meowed again.

The lady turned saying, "Hello Puss, do you want some dinner?" I stood frozen to the spot as she slowly approached and held out her hand. I waited to see what she would do next. Very slowly she moved closer and gently stroked my head. "Look George," she said, "I haven't seen this cat around before, and I wonder if he's lost." She slid her hand underneath me and lifted me up to show her husband. "He's a fine animal," remarked the man. "I expect he smelt dinner cooking. Looks like we have a guest!" A little time later they sat down to eat and I jumped up onto the seat beside the lady. She gave me a few titbits off her plate and said there was some cooling down for me to have later.

Sure enough, when they had finished their dinner she put a bowl of tasty fish and a saucer of milk outside the door for me. It didn't take long for me to devour the feast, then jump back inside and find my way onto the lady's lap. They obviously liked me, and I had a pleasant, comfortable evening with them. When it was time for them to go to bed, the lady put me outside and said she hoped to see me in the morning. It was warm and dry under their home, so I curled up there and went to sleep.

The following morning it was drizzling with rain. There was no sign of the sun or the hills, so I decided to stay where I was until the weather improved. The kindly couple opened a tin of fish for me for breakfast and gave me another saucer of milk. I heard them discussing what they should do with me, concerned that someone had lost me and wondering whether they should tell the police or take me to the local vet. They had a car parked beside their home and I was worried that I would be taken even further from mine. When the rain eased I wandered down to the riverbank where there were all sorts of boats moored in what looked like a kind of harbour. As you have probably gathered I'm not keen on water, so I explored around the back and discovered modern buildings with cars and boats on trailers parked alongside. There was nothing of interest to me so reluctantly I went back to where the elderly couple were living.

They had not made any decision about me, so I spent a comfortable day and evening with them. I fed well, I slept well and I awoke to see the sun rising over the horizon. It was time to be on my way again.

Feeling rested and refreshed, I crossed the road and headed over the fields towards the sunrise. The birds were singing and I made good time, gradually climbing away from the river.

As I reached the top of a rise I looked back and saw the hills, still large, but smaller than the last time I had seen them. However they looked different and I realised that during my day travelling down the other side of the river I had come too far downstream, so now I must change my direction to bring the hills back to the correct shape. This took me to another very busy road, and I had to wait for a gap in the traffic before crossing. Then I worked my way through a hedge and back across fields. I walked all day, keeping away from human habitation until, as evening approached, I entered a wood. I was weary, my bones ached from walking and this seemed to be a safe place to spend the night. Large birds roosted in the branches overhead and I found a fallen tree with a space underneath where I could curl up and feel secure. In moments, I fell into an exhausted sleep, too tired to even dream.

Sometime later something woke me up. I lay still and heard a soft rustling in the undergrowth accompanied by the musky, earthy, odour of some animal. I peered out and saw this large brownie-red animal with a bushy tail; Mr Fox was hunting pheasant for supper. I stayed quiet in my hiding place until all sound of him disappeared, and I could once again sleep in peace. In the morning I awoke refreshed and breakfasted on an unlucky young rabbit that popped out of his warren just as I was passing, then I continued on my way. I passed several villages but, knowing the dangers and not being hungry, I decided it was safer to keep away from humans.

I think it was on about the sixth or seventh day that I found myself approaching another town (Pershore). Climbing onto higher ground to avoid it, I once again saw the hills in the distance. They looked almost the same as they did from home, so I knew that I must be getting close. I had to cross several more roads before I left the town behind me, and I once more lost sight of the hills as I got back into the countryside. I was crossing a field when I spotted a stream. Could this be the Piddle Brook that led to my village? It smelt the same; perhaps if I followed it I would soon be home.

It took all day but then as I passed through yet another hedge, there it was, the field where the crows had stolen my first rabbit. And over the fence there was my home. Tiredness suddenly came over me and yet the relief at being so close kept me going. A few minutes later I was in my garden and going through the cat flap. There was no one around and no sign of my food or water bowls. But it didn't matter because all I wanted to do was sleep, so I curled up in the armchair and did just that.

The excitement in the household at my return had to be seen to be believed because everyone had assumed I was lost forever. There were tears of joy from Diane and the children. They fussed, cuddled, fed and groomed me and it was good to be home again, but I could never explain to them what I had been through to get there!

The following day I told Daisy about my adventure. She found it hard to believe that I had survived the town and managed to navigate my way home by the sun and the hills. Daisy, like most female cats, was a chatterbox and over the next few days news of my journey spread throughout the area, enhancing my reputation even further. One of the older cats dubbed me "The Marco Polo of the feline world", and once again I was the hero of the village.

Misty

CHAPTER SIX

A GROWING FAMILY

The days lengthened as May turned to June. The weather was now much warmer and I was able to spend most of my time out of doors hunting, returning home only in the evenings to keep the family company. My experiences had given me the confidence to travel much further from home in my hunt for quarry.

There were several farms within a couple of miles that I now visited – yes, there were farm cats about, but they had heard about me and gave very little trouble. The few cats that did try their luck soon learnt that it was best not to tangle with Sammy.

In early June the farmers started cutting the grass in their fields with huge mowers, leaving it to lie and dry in the warm sunshine. They followed these with machines that turned and lifted the drying grass, and a day or so later a huge noisy one that thumped along turning the grass into bales tied with string. Farm workers then loaded these bales onto trailers to be taken to the farms where they were unloaded into barns. This I discovered was how the hay where the rats and mice hid came to be where it was. The swallows were back, whirling in the sky as they caught insects. Birds were raising their young in nests hidden in trees and hedges, sometimes so intent on catching worms for them that they made easy prey. It seemed that once again all was well with the world: why is it that this is just when disaster strikes?

There was an air of excitement around the house. I watched as all sorts of clothing was packed into boxes with handles that were lying on a bed in a spare room. The family returned from shopping expeditions with new items that were carefully arranged on the bed. One evening as I was dozing on Rod's lap, he told me that I was going on holiday. I hadn't a clue what he was on about so I just carried on purring.

That evening when I went to go out of the cat flap, I found it locked and the litter tray had been put back down in the corner of the utility room. What was going on? Unconcerned, I climbed into my basket and slept soundly. The following morning Rod picked me up and bundled me into the box they used to take me to the vet, saying, "O.K. Sam, don't worry." Worry - I was terrified. Was I going to have more injections? I hoped not! Into the car we went and off we set. It wasn't long before we stopped and my box was lifted out of the car and carried into a strange-smelling place. A lady's voice gave instructions then a few moments later the box was opened and I jumped out. Where was I? Looking around I could see that I was surrounded by wire netting. Outside stood Rod and a cheerful lady who was assuring him that I would be all right. Rod put his finger through the mesh and scratched the top of my head, saying goodbye to me and adding that I would not be there for too long. Then he walked away with the lady.

I looked around my cage and noticed a ramp leading up to a wooden box; I cautiously climbed up this and found the floor of the box covered in wood shavings. In one corner there was a bowl of food and at the back a large shelf with a basket for sleeping. The whole place smelt of disinfectant, but at least it was warm and clean. Climbing back down the ramp I found a litter tray at the back of the cage, and again noticed that the floor was clean and dry. I heard other cats meowing then and became aware of many other cages with cats of all shapes and sizes looking at me. Next door were two very smart, cream-coloured Burmans who introduced themselves as Tom and Jerry. They were very friendly and realised that I was in some distress. They explained that they had been here several times before and that their owners always came to fetch them after a week or two. I wondered if this was punishment for something that I had done wrong, and if and when my family would ever come and fetch me.

A daily routine followed. The cheerful lady, I learnt that her name was Beryl, came every morning and evening, cleaned out my tray, changed my water and refilled my bowl with tinned food. The only variation was when people arrived either to collect cats or to bring new inmates. Every time a cat was collected, Beryl spent a long time washing out and disinfecting the house and cage before it was ready for the next occupant. At the end of the first week she washed down my run and changed the wood shavings in my sleeping compartment, being very careful not to let me escape through the door when she came and went. She was very kind, talking to each of us and giving us a cuddle every time she came to feed or clean us out. I noticed that she powdered and brushed every cat before it was collected by its owner.

A week passed and she powdered and brushed Tom and Jerry, and before long I bid farewell to my neighbours as their lady packed them into a travelling box and carried them away. An angry-looking and bad-tempered British Blue took their place and spent the next few days howling, crying and disturbing the rest of us.

At the end of the second week it was my turn to be powdered and brushed, and I realised that it must be time for me to go home. Rod arrived late in the afternoon looking much darker-skinned than when I had last seen him - which seemed very strange. He picked me up and cuddled me, kissing my head and saying how pleased he was to see me. He packed me into my travel box, said thank-you to Beryl, and put me into the car. After a short drive we arrived and Rod released me into the hall of my own home. Diane and the children also looked darker-skinned and healthier than when I had last seen them but I had no explanation for this phenomenon. I gathered that both they and I had been on what they referred to as a holiday. I hope that they enjoyed theirs more than I did mine.

I assumed that we would all quickly fall into our usual routine, but once again I was in for a shock: the following day they all set off in the car with my travel box, leaving me behind in the house with the cat flap locked so that I couldn't get out. They returned about an hour later. Rod carried the box into the lounge and carefully opened it. Imagine my surprise when the tiniest, skinniest little kitten you have ever seen crawled out. "Look, Sammy. We've brought you a friend," said Rod, picking the little creature up and bringing her towards me. I picked up a familiar smell. To begin with I couldn't place it, but suddenly it came rushing back to me: the barn where I had been born! Was this little kitten a relative, I wondered? She reminded me of my little sister who had died during those early days, but was much stronger than she had been. I jumped down from my chair and sniffed the newcomer, who promptly rolled onto her back to display her femininity. Rod picked me up and told me to be gentle with her as she was only a baby. He explained that, because I was such a wonderful companion to the family, they felt it was only fair that I should have a friend as well. I wasn't too sure about that, and wondered how things really would work out.

That evening they put the kitten into a cardboard box alongside my basket and left us together in the kitchen, telling me to look after the newcomer. As it became dark the little one began to whimper and cry, so I moved over and gave her a gentle wash.

She was soon purring contentedly and asked me who I was. I explained that I had once lived with my mother in a barn belonging to a kind lady called Mrs Roberts, and that these people had brought me to this wonderful place about a year ago. She squealed with excitement and told me that was where she came from! Slowly the truth dawned upon me: because they were so pleased and proud of me, the family had gone back to Mrs Roberts to find a companion for me. With trepidation I asked if she knew my mother, the beautiful black creature I had known for only a few weeks, or my father, the handsome and powerful character that I had only seen once. She told me excitedly that her mother was a similar colour to myself but much smaller, and that she understood my mother had died giving birth to a litter of kittens some time ago, none of which had survived. I was saddened by the news but I realised that I must now be the only one of my kind, unique in the world of cats! She told me that she had once seen her father who sounded exactly like mine, and that he had brought her mother a mouse only a few days ago. So this little kitten wasn't a stranger after all, she was my half-sister and, like it or not, it was my duty to look after her. I gently picked her up by the scruff of her neck and carried her to my basket saying, "Come on little sister, cuddle up to me and I'll keep you warm for the night." She soon fell asleep, and I closed my eyes, slept and dreamt of those early days.

My new companion had a loud purr that sounded like a motorcycle, so it wasn't long before my family named her Suki, which was short for Suzuki. For the next few weeks she was not allowed into the garden. I used the cat flap to come and go but she was neither big enough nor strong enough to push it open, so she stayed indoors. It didn't take long for me to become aware that Suki was fiercely independent; the more time passed the less notice she took of me, until I realised that she was even avoiding my company. She grew as the weeks passed, and eventually the back door was left open so that she could go into the garden. I offered to show her around but she refused the invitation, preferring to do her own exploring. Soon I realised that what she lacked in size she more than made up for in cunning and guile. Rather than allow me to accompany her and show her around, she had followed my scent and found the hunting places for herself!

A few days after she was allowed out I saw another strange looking Siamese-type male kitten about the same age as Suki, lying in the garden of a house just up the road. I decided to investigate and approached him boldly. He stood his ground, and I asked who he was and where he came from. Timidly, he told me that he had been brought here with his sister a few weeks ago. He was living with a lady and her daughters in this house and they called him Fred. I realised that he was Suki's brother, my half-brother, and that he might present more of a future problem to me than his sister. He was not as handsome as me, but quite muscular, and even then showed signs that he might grow into a fine animal; I would have to keep a close eye on Fred.

Suki was small and small she would always be, never a challenge to my superiority, but as a hunter and killer she was superb. Light and nimble on her feet, she had a speed that surprised even me, and a cunning way of lying in wait some distance from my own hiding places so that when I sprang for my prey she could ambush other rodents as they scattered. As the weeks passed, we developed a brilliant hunting system which lasted the rest of our lives without anyone ever being aware of it. Usually I would drive prey towards Suki, but sometimes the system worked in reverse when mice or birds settled closer to her, and she would drive them towards me. The outcome was very rewarding: we never missed a kill and often killed two at a time.

Suki had to undergo the same indignities as I had a year earlier. She went to the vet's for an operation to stop her having kittens, she was given various injections which she loathed, and both of us were regularly subjected to worming pills being forced down our throats. She slowly grew into a pretty little thing. Fred on the other hand grew larger and more muscular, eventually becoming about half as big again as Suki, but considerably shorter in the leg than me and nowhere near as large overall. So he did not materialise into the threat I had at first feared.

The warm, balmy days of summer faded as autumn approached. Suki grew steadily in size and confidence, continuing to become independent. In the house she now refused to have anything to do with me, sitting on a separate chair and spurning fuss from any of the family members. I still enjoyed human companionship, especially Rod's whose stroking I responded to with purrs, before falling asleep on his lap each evening. When they went to bed they now put Suki and I out through the front door and, weather permitting, we didn't return until after dawn. As time went on and this pattern was established, it became natural for us to become nocturnal hunters and to spend most of the daytime asleep indoors.

In the autumn, Suki had a fight with Fred. Both of them came away from it with scratches and bites that would leave scars on their faces and ears for the rest of their lives. More seriously, they loathed each other from then on and never associated again. I know that there are feuds in many families, but it was sad that she fell out with her own brother and never made up. I could not say that I was friendly with Fred. He respected my superiority and greater strength, and in acknowledgement of his loyalty I granted him the right to patrol and hunt the southern perimeter of the village without hindrance from me, and promised that I would help him to protect his territory from potential usurpers.

It was shortly after my agreement with Fred that Suki went missing. I came home one morning, not having seen her since we went out the previous evening. I had my dinner and then curled up and went to sleep in the chair in the lounge. When I awoke later in the day I was surprised not to see her in her usual place, curled up in the corner of the settee. I was not particularly concerned until the family returned in the evening and began to call her. As night approached and darkness fell, they became more and more concerned and went out looking for her and asking me where she was. I had no idea. As far as I was aware she hadn't followed me the previous night, which I had spent in Ginger's barn. With all the concern being shown in the household, I became somewhat worried myself and decided that, if she wasn't home by morning, I had better help in the search. Sure enough, when I awoke next morning her basket was still empty, so I crept quietly through the cat flap and set off.

My first thought was that she might have had an accident on the road, so I walked along the verge up to the bridge and looked along the bank of the stream and into the hedges and ditches. There was no sign of her at all. I talked to several other cats including Daisy, but no one had seen her during the past twenty four hours. I asked them to help in the search and to put word out that she was missing, so that all cats could be on the lookout for her.

I continued down the lane and found several old scent marks she had left. For a moment I thought this might be the direction she had taken but, other than the old scent, there was no trace of her. I knew that Suki was an independent female, but I was now coming to the conclusion that she was a S-catty kitten! I wondered whether she had come off worst in another fight with Fred, so I went round to his house and found him lying contentedly in the early morning sun. There was no sign of his having been in another fight, and he vigorously denied having seen any sign of Suki for the last couple of days.

As the hours passed and none of my feline friends found any sign of her, my concern grew. Darkness fell, and I returned home in the forlorn hope that she would return during the night. My family were still very upset at her disappearance and kept urging me to tell them where she was. Since I had already done my best, I curled up and fell into a dream-filled sleep.

Next morning she still hadn't returned. I was determined to organise proper search parties for her, so I patrolled the village asking every cat that I met to thoroughly search within designated areas. It was mid-afternoon when a farm cat from the eastern end of the village came running down the road to say he had found her but that he couldn't reach her.

Mystified, I followed him into his farmyard, past rusting machinery and through muddy puddles up to the closed door of a barn. "Suki," I shouted, and from behind the door I heard a faint and plaintive wail. "I'm here," she cried. "And I can't get out!" I told her to wait while I looked around. After a quick circuit of the barn I realised that there was only the one locked door, one window high up and no sign of any space where I could get in or Suki get out. I talked to her through the door and learnt that there were sacks of corn stored in the barn, plenty of mice and a few rats. She had been hunting here in what she considered to be her secret place when the farmer had come in with his tractor and trailer, frightening her so much that she had hidden behind the sacks. He had unloaded sacks of corn and left, closing the door behind him and locking her in.

I could see the tractor and trailer on the other side of the farmyard and wondered how long it would be before he delivered another load, giving her the opportunity to get out. Although she was frightened, she did have a good supply of food in the rats and mice, and there was water from a puddle of rainwater in the tractor-tyre tracks under the barn door. Whisky, the name of the farm cat who had found her, then broke the news that sometimes the barn was closed for weeks on end. What was I to do to get my poor half-sister released?

Telling Suki not to worry, I hurried home and tried to attract the attention of my family so as to get them to follow me and release her. I tried meowing at them, but they only seemed to think that I was hungry, thirsty or missing Suki. I rubbed up against their legs and walked to the door, but all they did was let me back out into the garden. I soon realised that they were not very intelligent and could not interpret what I was trying to tell them. What next?

I went back up to the farm to reassure Suki and to have a word with Whisky. I asked him when the farmer was likely to visit the barn, and he told me that he always came around in the morning to feed his horses and chickens. An idea was formulating in my mind. I told Suki and Whisky about it and then went off to have a word with Daisy, who reluctantly agreed to help. I asked her to gather as many of her friends as possible, and to meet me at the farmyard first thing in the morning.

As is the way of things, at dawn next day Daisy and Fred turned up on time, but sadly none of her other friends made an appearance. Whisky was there to meet us, so I explained my plan to them both and we waited by the barn for the farmer to arrive.

About an hour later a car drove into the yard and the farmer emerged and set of towards the stables at the far end. On my signal we all started howling at the top of our lungs, while I leapt up and down and scratched at the door.

The farmer stopped, then turned and walked towards us muttering about stupid cats and what the devil were we up to? As he got closer, Daisy and Fred fled as fast as their paws would carry them. I was terrified that he would throw something at me, but I stood my ground and kept on howling and scratching at the door.

"Now what have we got going on here?" he said. "Who's your friend, Whisky? I haven't seen him around before!" Then, to my great relief he took some keys from his pocket, inserted one into the lock, turned it and in moments was swinging the heavy door open. As he did so, Suki scampered out between his legs and ran across the yard towards home. "Well bless my soul!" he shouted. "That kitten could have been in there for weeks. That's the strangest thing I ever did see!" He put his hand down and stroked my head, murmuring that he didn't know cats could be so clever. I purred and slowly backed away, thanking Whisky for all his help.

I walked quickly down the road and into our house where they were all making a great fuss of Suki. I went up to her and gave her a lick of welcome. But I was disappointed to realise that they would never know it was due to me that she was home. Oh well, I suppose all's well that ends well.

The Cats' House

CHAPTER SEVEN

AS TIME GOES BY

As the seasons came and went in swift succession, I grew to full maturity, gaining a few scars from minor skirmishes with new arrivals in the village, and a few from squirrels and rats that stood and fought for their lives. Suki became an adult, small in size but probably the next best hunter to myself. We still hunted together at night but Fred never joined us. Despite helping to rescue Suki, he had never made up with her and went about his business without troubling us. Higgins, the liver and white springer spaniel who lived opposite, was taken ill and died, and a year or two later Daisy passed away. This was a great sadness to me; Daisy had been my first friend in the village and had taught me so many things as I grew up. Now that she had gone I missed her and realised that she was the one cat that I had loved. There had always been a bond between us, not recognised as love and never expressed. Sadly, it was now too late to tell her, but I would forever carry her memory in my heart.

We had one very cold winter when the snow fell heavily after Christmas and lasted for several weeks. It was so deep that we found it difficult to walk outside. The children loved it, wrapping themselves up in warm clothes, building snowmen in the garden and throwing snowballs at each other. Suki and I however spent the time indoors curled up in front of the log-burning stove: there is no fun in frozen paws.

We were very happy, even though the children grew bigger and took less and less notice of us. Occasionally in summer the family packed their suitcases and we knew that they would soon be off on holiday again. There was a game I used to play when the cases were nearly packed: I would climb into one of them and make believe that I wanted to go on holiday with my family. They soon came to realise that I knew when they were going away and thought that I didn't want them to go. They no longer sent us to the cattery, instead they made arrangements with a neighbour to come in and give us food and water, and apart from that, we were left to our own devices.

I must have been about eight years old when more changes started to happen. The family went off one day with the empty cat basket and returned a few hours later with two new kittens, silver-grey Tabby Persians with strange flat faces, green eyes, shiny black lips and beautiful coats. They named the boy Whisper and the girl Misty. They were very tiny and Suki and I decided that it would be best to ignore them rather than risk getting into trouble. At first they were nervous and timid, but as they grew they became more playful and bold. After a few weeks they were let out into the garden for the first time, and it became apparent to me that, although they were very distinctively marked, they had not been bred to be hunters like myself and the other cats in the village. Put this together with my opinion that they were not very bright, and I could see trouble looming. Misty, like Suki, developed into a small female despite being sent to the vets to be spayed. Whisper, on the other hand, matured into a large and strong neutered male almost incapable of catching either bird or mouse.

Suki had found a favourite spot under a large shrub beside the lawn where, unseen by anyone, she could lie in wait for unwary prey. Her colouring blended in perfectly with the earth and branches, forming an excellent camouflage. Unsuspecting birds would land in search of earthworms and as soon as they hopped within range she would pounce, hardly ever failing to despatch another sparrow or starling. Whisper and Misty must have watched her and, not realising how their colouring differed, believed that they could have equal success. I observed with amusement as they tried their best. Whisper was by far the most comical. He would lie in wait in the flower bed or under a bush and as soon as a bird landed he would flatten himself ready to pounce. The excitement would quickly become too much for him and he would quiver all over and wag his tail like a flag in a gale. The birds immediately saw him and flew away. As time went by they got wiser and, knowing he was there, would torment him by hopping around just out of range. Whisper would charge out in frustration and always miss his target by inches. Misty was a little more cunning and at least she was able to keep still. So she did make the occasional kill.

Winter came and went again and the Persians grew. They began losing their winter coats as summer approached. Whisper's was sleek and shiny and he developed the most magnificent plumed tail, but Misty's was much coarser and her tail was nowhere near as impressive. She needed grooming every day, and lost so much fur from her body and face that she began to look quite wretched. I felt a bit sorry for her.

Misty and Whisper had little success hunting in the garden and little more in the wilderness next door. It was therefore almost inevitable that as their confidence grew they would start to roam further and further from home. I warned the other village cats to leave them alone, and this helped to keep them out of trouble and fights. They soon found that hunting together brought greater rewards, but since Misty was lighter and more nimble she still had a greater kill rate than Whisper. He eventually became jealous and fell out with her. From then on they did most of their hunting separately.

That summer, builders arrived and constructed a sun lounge at the back of the living room. It was furnished with small tables and very comfortable chairs, and since it caught the afternoon sun it was a fine place for us to enjoy a nap. However, since there were only four chairs and we occupied them all, there was often a rude awakening when the family decided to use the room and forcibly removed us so that they could sit in our chairs themselves.

By their second summer, Whisper and Misty were full-grown and roaming the village full of confidence. I have to admit that Whisper had turned into a magnificent cat. I once heard him described as looking like a white tiger, and perhaps that was true. He walked with a swagger, his tail held high, and he really was quite impressive. It was a pity his brains didn't match his looks - and after all they do say that pride comes before a fall.

It was in mid-summer that tragedy struck. I came home one Saturday morning after a night's hunting to find everyone in the house distraught. It seemed that a car had killed Whisper.

His body was laid on a table in the garden with no mark on it except for a little blood by his mouth. I could see tears in Misty's eyes, and both children and adults were crying. His body was placed into a wicker basket. A hole was dug in the garden under an apple tree, then the basket was placed in it and covered with earth. Finally, a large flat stone was put over his resting place. That night Suki and Misty joined me, as we sat under the tree saying our last goodbyes to our friend.

A few weeks later the family came home with a new Silver Tabby Persian kitten who was about twenty weeks old. It transpired that his owner had sent him to another home but because he was too mischievous they had sent him back. This kitten was eventually named Toby, and they introduced him to us as a friend for Misty. Toby was a very playful kitten but Misty seemed to accept his playfulness with only the odd cuff to keep him in place when he overstepped the mark. Suki and I decided it was wisest to ignore him.

Another change took place as a result of the death of Whisper: my family no longer allowed Misty to go outside, and Toby was kept indoors with her. I think they must have finally realised that the Persians did not have as much road sense as Suki and myself, because we were still allowed to roam free. The cat flaps were set so that although we could get into the house, we now had to meow at the door to be let out - which was a bit tiresome after all this time. However we soon got used to it.

Toby was a very different character to Whisper, although he did have similar green eyes, a fine coat and a very bushy tail. I don't know what it was, but he seemed to have a comical face and he was the clumsiest cat I ever came across. Cups, vases and ornaments went flying as he charged around. Yes he was fast, but he was very heavy on his feet, and since he was kept indoors, he was constantly getting into trouble.

The next arrival was a different matter all together. Danny was brought into the household the following summer. He was about sixteen weeks old, a Blue-point Birman, strong and arrogant, and unlike previous arrivals, he was not at all nervous or submissive. On his first evening he raised his hackles to me of all cats. So I cuffed him and told him to clear off. Within an hour he had scratched Toby's nose, hissed at Suki, chased Misty and generally had the house in turmoil. Things didn't improve over the next few days as he terrorised the others in an attempt to dominate the household. It was therefore a great relief when we saw him put into the cat basket and taken away. Imagine our surprise when later that day the family returned with yet another kitten, a Blue-point Birman named Pickwick, totally different to the terrorist who had just departed. He was sensibly submissive when he arrived in the house, rolling over onto his back and showing strange pink pads on his feet as soon as any of us approached, and keeping away from trouble. He had a cream coat and the most beautiful china-blue eyes and, as we were to find out, a very laid back nature, keen to avoid trouble at any cost. He was much the same age and size as Toby, and it seemed very natural that the two of them should get on well together and play as kittens do. Toby spent much of his time preening Pickwick. After this strenuous activity they would curl up and sleep together.

In the spring of the following year a new construction started in the garden. One of the two pear trees was cut down and concrete slabs laid on the ground between the remaining pear tree and an apple tree. A wooden house was erected on the slabs and a frame covered in wire netting with a gate in the side attached to it. A shelf was laid on the top of the pear tree stump that had been left in the middle of this construction and shelves were put around the sides. I noticed a cat flap leading from the wooden house into the run. A little later they put shelves into the house and covered them and the floor in carpet. When all of this was finished, they gathered up Misty, Toby and Pickwick and placed them inside, telling them that this was to be their daytime residence. A new routine was now established that suited me very well. Every morning the Persians and

Pickwick were carried out to the run and locked in with food and water provided. In the evening they were taken back indoors to spend time with the family, before being put in the utility room for the night. This meant that once again the cat flaps were left open in the daytime for Suki and myself.

Our home now consisted of five cats: myself and Suki, both Seal-point part Siamese, Misty and Toby, both Silver-Tabby Persians, and Pickwick, a Blue-point Birman. It therefore came as no surprise when a year later we were joined by another Blue-point Birman to match Pickwick. This latest arrival was named Dickens, so now there were six of us. He was very small, and at first slept at night in the upstairs shower room. He was sensibly submissive and somewhat frightened of the rest of us, so we all chose to ignore him.

On a fine sunny afternoon a few weeks after his arrival, I was sleeping in my usual chair in the sun lounge when Dickens came in, spotted me and jumped into a chair on the other side of the room, then curled up and fell into a contented sleep. An hour or two later Pickwick and the Persians were brought into the house from their outdoor home. A few minutes after that Toby ambled into the sun lounge, Dickens opened his eyes and watched as Toby approached, sniffed at him and then, to my amazement, climbed gently onto Dickens' chair and started to lick him all over. Dickens rolled onto his back and started to purr. I realised that I was witnessing something very special because here was our comical, clumsy companion finally finding his purpose in life. From then on, Toby became the father figure of the feline household. I might be senior cat, but he was the one who wanted to look after the others.

I was lying in my chair thinking about what I had witnessed when I suddenly realised that I was now around ten years old and that to Toby, Pickwick and Dickens I must be like a grand-father cat. It was a shock to realise that I was getting on, and yes perhaps I did have a few aches and pains and did spend a few hours longer in the chair indoors, and did get up more slowly in the morning. That afternoon I wandered down to the river and for the first time for many years looked at my reflection in the calm water. Gazing back at me was a stranger, the image of the father I had seen once so many years ago. I realised that the slightly battle-scarred face framed by a few grey hairs and whiskers was mine, and that the once youthful face had been replaced by one of character and experience, mellowed with age but still handsome and proud. It was a good thing I had left Toby with the responsibility for the "indoor cats"; I still had enough to do looking after my territory.

It also turned out to be a wise move because Toby took his responsibility very seriously. Gone was the tearaway kitten, replaced by a caring and considerate young cat, and this made humans and cats love him all the more. Within days Misty and Pickwick were treating Toby with more respect and Dickens was able to join them in their outdoor home during the daytime. From that day onwards I never saw a fight between any of them.

There were occasions when one or other of the young cats would escape from captivity and everyone would be out searching for the absentee, but fortunately there were no more accidents on the road. Misty, who had known freedom, wandered the furthest on these occasions, seeking out her old hunting grounds. But the others stayed close to our own garden, and the escapee always managed to reappear for food sooner or later.

With their routine established they became very happy in their daytime accommodation and began to treat it as their second home. I watched them grooming each other and bonding as a real family. Pickwick would sometimes become restless and pace backwards and forwards indicating that he wanted to be let back into the house, but his ruse seldom worked, and eventually he would settle down and go to sleep. Considering the variety of breeds, it was amazing how well we all got on together, Suki and I living quite independent lives and the others happy with theirs as house cats.

Two years later we had another addition to our family, a huge Seal-point Ragdoll kitten with a black face and coat similar to my own. They called him Harley. As soon as I saw him I knew that here was a cat with the potential to take over from me if he was ever given the opportunity to do so. By the size of his paws it was obvious that he was going to be very large, and he was more intelligent than any other cat I had ever met, although strange in many ways. He bonded with the humans more than any of us, following them around and enjoying their company rather than that of his companions.

Toby of course, as father of the family, was the first to welcome him into the fold and protected him from some spiteful approaches by the two females, Suki and Misty. Perhaps I should point out that my observations of the females of my species showed that although they were smaller than us males, they made up for lack of size by being far more aggressive.

Whilst Suki was my half-sister and it suited me to hunt with her, I can hardly say that we were close friends; she was far too independent for that. Misty was much the same: although living in close proximity to the others she maintained her independence and was the only one I ever heard hissing and spitting at any of them. The boys always got on well together, and with Toby's help Harley was soon accepted by the Birmans.

Pickwick

CHAPTER EIGHT

OLD AGE AND CHANGING TIMES

A year later my aches and pains had increased, I was slowing down and not patrolling as far and wide as I had once done. Even Suki was beginning to show signs of age; she had become very thin and started to complain of aching joints and pains in her stomach. During the summer of that year I met her brother Fred, and was shocked to see how ill he looked. I told

Suki about this, and it came as little surprise when we heard a few weeks later that he had died very suddenly of a suspected heart attack.

It was at about this time that big changes began to take place in our village. Workmen appeared and demolished the dilapidated old buildings in the wilderness behind our garden. A new barn was erected closer to the black and white house; the bushes, brambles and undergrowth were cleared, and all chances of hunting disappeared.

Shortly afterwards, the workmen moved over the road to the farm where we had hunted all of our lives. They took the hay and straw out of the Dutch barn, dismantled it and cleared the ground all around. They then demolished the small buildings surrounding the farmyard, so that yet another hunting ground was taken from us. Over the next few months building work commenced and, by the next spring, there was a brand new house and garden where the wilderness had once been. The brick Jubilee barn by the old farmyard had also been converted into a large house. These may have been nice for humans, but we had lost our closest and favourite hunting places.

Harley was by now a fine figure of a cat, larger than me with big blue eyes and a superb tail. He had never been allowed to roam free and so he had not been given the chance to take over from me, despite his size and undoubted ability. Because of his attentiveness to humans, they became very fond of him and gave him more than his fair share of attention. Then I noticed that he began to sit on his own and breathe quickly and shallowly, and I realised that all was not well despite his size and strength. Over the weeks he began to eat and drink less, and soon his coat lost some of its lustre. Eventually he was taken to the vet's and given some sort of injection, but he showed no sign of improvement. Two weeks later he became very distressed, and Rod and Diane rushed him back to the vet's, but when they returned it was without him. Once again there were tears and distress in the household, and we learnt that our youngest companion had died while having an operation. A few days later in a little ceremony, the family buried a small casket containing his ashes beside Whisper, under the apple tree.

I suppose that inevitably a replacement for Harley would be found. The family went off on holiday in mid-summer, and shortly after their return another Seal-point Ragdoll called Danny joined us.

Why they called him Danny after our first experience of a cat of that name I never understood, but this Danny was quite a different matter. He was large for a kitten. Not as large as Harley, but he bonded with humans in just the same way. Toby repeated his performance of father cat, and in no time at all Danny was accepted by the others. He grew into a fine cat, and was much healthier than Harley. Sometimes when I looked at him I could see a younger version of myself standing there. He was heavier than I ever was, but he had a similar round face with black mask and blue eyes. I sometimes thought him to be more dog than cat because of the way he followed the human family around. And he talked to them. Of course they didn't seem to understand him. But that didn't stop him constantly mewing in his own distinctive way asking for food or company. He became quite spoilt. He was the first of the cats to be allowed to climb onto the bed, and he would charge upstairs at every opportunity in the hope of being allowed into the bedroom.

As winter drew on I became aware of a nagging pain in my stomach, I lost some of my appetite and I had a perpetual thirst. I no longer had the energy to go out hunting and preferred to spend most of my time indoors. In fact I was so concerned with my own aches and pains that I didn't take much notice of Suki. She seemed to spend more and more time out of doors despite the cold winter weather, but I assumed that she had found a new friend or fresh hunting grounds. She appeared quite healthy, so I was not particularly concerned when she failed to come home one morning.

As had happened so long ago, she was missing for several days, but this time I hadn't the energy to go searching for her because deep inside me I knew that something terrible had happened.

She was found dead several days later on a pathway not far from our home. There were no signs of her having been in an accident, although she appeared to have been running when she died. It was a mystery like Fred. Had they both suffered from some heart defect that killed them within months of each other, or had they picked up some poison? We were never to know. Poor Suki, she was buried at the bottom of our garden, not under the apple tree with Whisper and Harley. I think she would have approved of her final resting place; she had been a solitary cat all her life, with me as her only friend and companion.

I miss Suki, and I miss the hunting grounds that have disappeared. I am almost fifteen years old and tiring of life. I have loved two cats, Daisy and Suki, and I miss them both; I know that I will soon be joining them wherever they are. I don't know where we go when we die. I wonder if we come back here. If so what will I be? Maybe a butterfly, maybe a bird, maybe a human, but if I have a choice I would come back as me again.

The pain in my stomach is getting much worse. It's more severe after I have eaten, which rather puts me off my food. Perhaps it is time to reflect on my human family before it is too late.

Dickens

CHAPTER NINE

THOUGHTS ON HUMANS

I have been lucky to have had so many perfect days. Now in the twilight of my life, I have settled into a cosy routine in which I spend most of my days sleeping in one of the warm armchairs or in the sunshine on the patio, waiting for the family to come home. My evenings are spent in the lounge enjoying the human company and eventually jumping onto Rod's lap, treading and being stroked, purring with pleasure and falling asleep. Finally, when the family want to go to bed, I am put outside the front door to spend the night hunting or sleeping in one of the barns. They leave the cat flap open so that I can go into the kitchen to escape from inclement weather. Of late I have had plenty of time to observe my human companions, so what do I really think about you?

First, you all smell. I know that sounds rude, but I keep clean by licking myself, and I only pick up the odours of my surroundings. You humans however bathe in perfumed water, you wash your hair in scented shampoo and your females spray theirs with the strangest-smelling lacquer. You cover yourselves in different aromas to try to make yourself smell better, then you stroke me and transfer them to me, and you wonder why I keep washing myself! Well I'm trying to rid myself of your smell! What self-respecting cat can go hunting successfully smelling like that?

Not only do you constantly wash and bathe in the soapy stuff, you are always laundering your clothes to try to get your own smells off them. You have a washing machine and tumble dryer that seem to be on the go everyday, and there are always clothes either hanging on the line outside or on racks on the landing. I'm not suggesting that you should go about naked, from what I have seen you don't have any hair to cover your bodies so they are pink, fat and ugly, but I would have thought that by now you could have developed some sort of disposable body covering rather than using all that detergent which finishes up killing the fish and causes suds in our brook. I would not exchange my fine fur coat for any of your fancy clothes. It keeps me warm in winter, protects me from the rain, is easily cleaned and looks better than anything that you wear. Somewhere along the line you seem to have got the idea that you own us felines. Well I have news for you; we have always been in charge! When did you last eat a meal brought to you by one of us? Yet we regularly send you out shopping to bring tasty food to us. Do we groom you? No. But we have you trained to brush and comb us and get rid of the knots in our coats! Do we empty litter trays? Do we clean up our dirty paw prints? Do we brush the cat hair off the chairs? Do we make our own beds? Do we worry when you go out? Do we pay the bills? Who spends an evening being petted and stroked? Do we come when you call? No, we rule the roost and we know it!

You do the most extraordinary and unnatural things like smoking and polluting the atmosphere. How is a cat supposed to retain a sense of smell when you subject us to rooms full of burning tobacco? You may be unaware of the food odours you carry around with you from your kitchens and dining rooms. Why, even your breath smells of the spices in the unhealthy cooked food you eat!

I have become aware of how poor are your senses of smell, hearing and eyesight. I can sniff out a bird's nest in any hedge, I can hear a mole digging his underground tunnel and I can see a mouse move in a bale of straw at one hundred yards. You can never experience the joy of watching the acrobatic flight of bats at night or an owl in the moonlight swoop from high on a branch to pluck a small rodent from the dark ground below.

You have become soft in your centrally-heated houses. You eat too much of the wrong things, you take little exercise and then complain of being overweight. You go from door to door in your awful, dangerous cars with never a thought for your environment. Do you ever wonder why the brilliant green of the hedges and byways fades so quickly? Does it never occur to you that the smoke from the exhaust of your cars damages the leaves and grasses every time you pass? How often do you feel pity for the dead bird or animal lying by the roadside, killed by someone hurrying on their way to who knows where? You humans seem to us an unseeing, unhearing and uncaring breed, determined to seek only your own comfort and self-gratification.

I used to wonder why my family had taken me into their home, until I heard it explained that stroking a cat was a form of relief from tension. Don't get me wrong - I like being stroked. But think about it: the only reason they took me in was to relieve the stress caused by their own lifestyle. Doesn't that say it all!

I don't want to sound bitter because I'm not. I have probably got the best life of any cat on earth, and I know that there are many of us living in awful conditions. I was lucky to have found a family who are kind and very loving towards me. No, it is me who feels sorry for them. My family always seems to be rushing from here to there, to work or to school, to get meals ready, to go out, never a minute to relax and only sleeping for seven or eight hours a day before rushing off again. I think I know who has the best life, and it's not them. I have a leisurely life. You will never see me hurry to anything other than my dinner bowl. I take my time when I eat, I have plenty of sleep, I can amuse myself stalking and hunting, and I am happy.

When my family took me into their home, they had no idea about cats. They learnt about my needs from reading books and because I instructed them about my likes and dislikes. But I realise that they came to love me and all of the other cats who have joined us even more than we love them. I first realised this when poor Whisper was killed. Rather than accepting it as fate, the whole family was distressed for days. They buried him in a wicker basket in the garden. For the first time I saw humans weeping, and I appreciated the emotion they felt for us. It happened again when Harley was taken sick and never returned from the vet's surgery. Tears and sobbing seemed to go on for days. More recently, they wept again after Suki's mysterious death. It made me realise just how much these humans love us cats, and on reflection I suppose that this family would not have made a home for the nine of us who have lived here unless they really did so. Perhaps my family are special in devoting so much time and attention to us, and we on our part accept our domesticated state and enjoy the freedom that they give us.

We have learnt to live with each other, you accepting our short-comings and occasional failures, and we sharing our love with you and accepting your peculiarities.

Good Companions

EPILOGUE – Author's Note

Sammy's dying days were almost as extraordinary as the life he had led. It became apparent in the late spring of 2000 that he was not well because he no longer left the house, he ate very little and he was drinking copious amounts of water.

We noticed that although he had lost body weight, his stomach was slightly distended and seemed very tender to the touch. One Friday, with fear and trepidation, we took him to the vet's to find out what was wrong with him. After much probing, Xrays and blood tests, we were sent away and told that we would get the results early the next week. The telephone call we were all dreading came on the following Tuesday. Sammy had an inoperable tumour and the vet suggested that as a kindness to him we had him put to sleep sooner rather than later. It was not a decision we could make quickly, and as he did not seem to be in too much pain, we decided to wait on events.

On Thursday of the same week Sammy disappeared. We hunted high and low, but we could not find any trace of him. I telephoned the vet to tell him, and he said it was not unusual for a cat to take itself off to die. Remembering how Suki had disappeared and been found dead close to home, we continued to search for him. Every morning I would go to the front door expecting him to be there waiting for his food, but the days passed and after a week we resigned ourselves to the inevitable and gave up the search. We were all very sad to have lost him without a chance to say our goodbyes.

Then, exactly two weeks to the day after his disappearance, I glanced through the front window and saw him sitting on the drive. At first I thought it was his ghost, and then I shouted "Sammy's home!" Everyone came running as I opened the door and went out to pick him up. I soon realised that he was in distress, and that, wherever he had been, it had taken a supreme effort to drag himself home. As I lifted him up I heard that wonderful purr. I took him into the lounge, sat down, put him gently onto my lap and, with tears in my eyes, vowed that as long as he had a purr left in him he would stay with us. He had been brave enough to get home, and here he should stay.

Try as we might over the next few days, we could not get him to eat or drink, so that by the following Monday he was so weak that the purring finally stopped. I was alone at home, so I telephoned Diane at work to tell her that the dreadful moment had at last arrived.

Once again barely able to control my tears, I placed him gently in the travel basket, and drove slowly to the vet's surgery. As I took him from the car I said my final goodbye, and offered thanks to him and to God for a friendship that I would remember for the rest of my life.

Sammy's ashes are interred alongside Suki at the bottom of our garden, and a rose named "Remembrance" has been placed over them. It is a quiet spot on the edge of his territory, shaded by trees and next to where his favourite wilderness once was. Sometimes I go and talk to him and remember how he was, and I still shed a tear for my brave and faithful friend.

- - - - - - - - - -

Truth, it is said, is stranger than fiction; the chapter The Adventure is based upon Sammy's disappearance from home for two weeks following a visit from a television repairman who was based in Malvern. Whether he did climb into his van will forever be a mystery, but it is quite possible.

In July of 2003, three years after Sammy's death, we decided to have a boundary fence replaced. I contacted Steve, a local fencing man, and he arrived with his lorry and a colleague on Tuesday 8th July. They proceeded, with a great deal of noise and disruption, to demolish the old fence and prepared the ground for new fence posts. That evening, Toby, by now nine years old but still a comedian and the daddy cat to the other four, failed to return home.

We waited up until midnight, finally going to bed and leaving the cat flap open for him. He had not returned by the following morning, and we were all by now very concerned for his safety, thinking that the previous day's hectic and noisy activity had frightened him away. Steve and his colleague arrived just after breakfast the next day and, when asked, said they had not seen Toby anywhere.

Diane went to work while I spent the day looking along the roadside and asking neighbours if they had seen our missing cat, but to no avail. Late in the afternoon the workmen completed the job and said they would keep an eye out for Toby along the local lanes. On Thursday we telephoned all of the local vets, the Cats Protection League and the police to report Toby missing. We walked for miles searching the hedgerows and ditches, to no avail. Finally we produced a leaflet which we dropped through every door in the village, asking everyone to look in their sheds and garages in case he was locked in. The weather that week was incredibly hot. The thermometer in my greenhouse went up to 110 degrees even with the door and windows open, and we were concerned that if Toby were locked in somewhere, he would stand little chance of survival. The days passed and we continued to search far and wide with no success. Diane rang Steve and asked him to double-check his lorry, which he did, but he said that there was no sign of him.

By the weekend we were beginning to lose hope, and our concern was not just over the loss of a family member. It was not knowing what had happened to him that caused extra distress. We began to wonder whether a fox or mink had taken him, or even if there was some larger predator in the area. We spent the weekend retracing our steps around the village and widening our search area, but without success. The heatwave continued and by Tuesday 15th July, just when we had given up hope of ever seeing him again, the doorbell rang and there on the doorstep was Steve looking very upset.

He enquired whether we had found our cat to which I replied "No." "I think he's in my lorry," he said. I immediately asked whether he was dead. "I'm so sorry," he stated. I asked how he had found him and he said that he had seen him on his driver's seat that morning when he was about to go to work. "Is he alive?" I exclaimed. "Oh yes," he said. I rushed to the passenger side of the lorry cab, and with his help we removed piles of tools, coats and other articles from in front of the seat, but I could see no sign of Toby. Steve pointed out some cat hair and said Toby was hiding under the seat. On looking closely, I discovered a small gap, and peering in I could just see the top of Toby's back behind a bulkhead. I put my arm into the gap and finally managed to grab hold of his neck and pull him out. He was alive, but only just. His eyes seemed to be out of focus and all gummed up, and his body was thin and emaciated. I thanked a still-apologising Steve, telling him that it was not his fault, and rushed Toby indoors. We put him down and gave him a bowl of water before ringing the vet. He drank and drank, but the vet said to give him as much as he wanted and that he would probably be all right in a few days.

And so he was. After plenty to eat and drink and a bath, he looked and smelt better. Over the next few days he put on weight and within a couple of weeks he had made a full recovery. How he survived seven days in the boiling hot cab of that lorry is a near miracle. No doubt he used up a few of his nine lives, and he now certainly appreciates his home more than ever.

We contacted everyone in the village again to tell them that Toby had been found, and they were all delighted to hear of his safe return.

So perhaps Sammy's adventure does have some truth in it after all.

Danny

DANNY'S POSTSCRIPT

Although Sammy has gone, we other cats remember him with love and affection. He was brave, handsome, cunning and strong. Sammy was the first cat in our home and he initially greeted each new arrival with disdain and indifference. We learnt of his reputation from others, but we soon realised that despite his superior ways he protected us from a distance, so perhaps he did care for us in his own way. Toby maintains his role of father figure to us all, and is still loved by everyone.

For some reason the family must have decided that it was no longer necessary for us to spend our days confined to the cats' house outside during the daytime, because one morning the gate was opened and we were ushered into the garden. I had never known freedom before, so explored the hedge, lawn and flower beds with great interest. Misty still wanders further afield but keeps out of trouble. Toby, Pickwick and Dickens, like me, are content to stay within our own garden. Strangely enough, I often go back into our run and sit on a shelf in the shade because I consider this to be cat territory! We can go into the house whenever we want, but now sleep in our outdoor home at night. I'm sure Sammy would have approved of the new arrangement.

I'm often told that I look like Sammy. I'm by far the youngest in our household, but I'm the largest and cleverest of all. Everyone loves me, and if I am a bit like Sammy then I shall try to live up to his reputation.

Danny April 2005

CHRONOLOGY

Sammy (Samurai) Cross Bred Siamese   Born April 1985
Died May 8th 2000

Suki (Suzuki)   Cross Bred Siamese   Born May 1987
Died January 15th 2000

Whisper   Silver Tabby Persian   Born October 1992
Died August 1994

Misty   Silver Tabby Persian   Born October 1992

Toby   Silver Tabby Persian   Born March 1994

Danny   Blue-point Birman   Born April 1994
Returned to breeder

Pickwick   Blue-point Birman   Born April 1994

Dickens   Blue-point Birman   Born August 1995

Harley   Seal-point Ragdoll   Born April 1997
Died 5th June 1999

Danny   Seal-point Ragdoll   Born March 1999